rockets through SPACE

The Story of Man's Preparations to Explore the Universe

BY LESTER DEL REY

Illustrated by James Heugh

A SCIENCE-FACT BOOK

THE JOHN C. WINSTON COMPANY · *Philadelphia · Toronto*

FIRST EDITION

Made in the United States of America

L. C. Card #57-8844

To

A. J. BUDRYS

for past, present and future

other books to read

There are some other books which are well worth reading, if you want to learn still more about our next steps into space.

The Conquest of Space, by Willy Ley, with illustrations by Chesley Bonestell (The Viking Press, Inc.), gives a great deal of information on our whole Solar System, and shows how a trip through space can take place. There are a great many beautiful pictures in this book.

Across the Space Frontier and *The Conquest of the Moon,* edited by Cornelius Ryan. *The Conquest of Mars,* by Wernher von Braun and Willy Ley. These three titles, published by The Viking Press, Inc., are more complete versions of the articles that appeared in *Collier's* magazine. These three give the full details of Dr. Wernher von Braun's plans for the space station, the trip to the Moon and the trip to Mars. Each book also includes excellent articles by other writers as well as a large number of superb illustrations. All three books should be read by anyone who wishes to know more about future projects in space.

The Exploration of Space, by Arthur C. Clarke (Harper & Brothers), is one of the best and most comprehensive general works on our future in space.

The Exploration of the Moon, by Arthur C. Clarke and illustrated by R. A. Smith (Harper & Brothers), shows many illustrations of what our future on the Moon will be, together with short articles. It contains very good details on the building of a colony on the Moon.

Finally, for those who wish to learn more about the history of the rocket, exactly how it works and how the early rocket societies operated (as well as almost any other data on rockets), there is *Rockets, Missiles and Space Travel,* by Willy Ley (The Viking Press, Inc.). This is a long and sometimes technical book, but no other volume quite equals it.

up from earth

IN THE FUTURE, schools will probably have courses in space and space travel, just as boys and girls are now taught all about other lands in their geographies. Unfortunately, teaching of such courses lies several years ahead. Today, anyone who wants to learn more than the simplest facts about rockets and elementary astronomy has a very hard time finding the information.

There are books which contain the answers, but these are too often filled with mathematics and complicated science too hard for the general reader to understand. There are also some books that are easy to read, but most of these do not give enough answers to the questions we want answered.

I have found every time I talk before a group of science-minded listeners there are quite a few of those questions which need answers. How can we be sure a rocket will push a ship when there is "no air to push against"? That is the most common question, but there are many others.

What will hold a space station up, after we build it? How high is space? How dangerous are meteors? Is space freezing cold or boiling hot? What about life on other worlds? If we can't see the other side of the Moon, why can't there be life there? If a station is only a thousand miles up, why won't the people inside it feel the pull of Earth? Will there be space wars? Can we ever fly to the stars?

These questions need full answers. To give those answers, as well as all the information to cover fully the other questions about space, is the purpose of this book.

It is not meant as a textbook. Instead, it is really an adventure story. It deals with an adventure that has not happened yet, but one that will begin almost at once. Going out into space will be the greatest adventure of all time. Nothing else men have done can compare with it. Even the voyage of Columbus across the ocean was less adventurous than the first trip to another planet will be.

The only event that could compare to such a breaking away from the surface of Earth was something done by a fish, if the scientists are right. According to what many scientists believe, that fish (called a Crossopterygian, or lobe fin) came out of the water and moved about in air a long time ago. This would make him the greatest of all pioneers, since he and his children changed from a life in water to a life in air—almost like a man changing from a life in our air to one in space.

Of course, the fish did not know what he was doing. By our standards, he was an ugly, stupid creature. He was not even a very remarkable fish. He was not big or very active; he probably was not even very brave; and he certainly was not the best fighter among fishes.

He was probably something like the modern lungfish. He lived in the shallows of fresh-water streams. When these dried up in the hot summer Sun, he holed up in the mud at the bottom, barely staying alive by sucking a tiny bit of air through the small quantity of water he kept with him. To do this, he learned to use his air bladder—the sac most fishes use to adjust for depth, like the tanks of a submarine—as a very crude, inefficient lung to help his gills.

But he learned to take oxygen directly from the air, instead of from the small amount dissolved in water, and this trick made it possible for him to learn to live on dry land.

Maybe it was a good thing he was not able to talk about what he was going to do. Imagine what might have happened if he and all his friends had been intelligent. Think of them swimming around discussing it when he first said he would like to get out of water and see what land was like. . . .

"Impossible. Can't be done," his father Rhipidistian snorted. "Nothing to breathe up there. You'd have to carry your water with you. You'd need a suit filled with it, or you'd probably explode. Don't you realize it's *empty* up there?"

Cousin Coelacanth shook his head sadly. "You're crazy. You couldn't even move around. No water to push against!"

"Besides, what good would it do you? You've got everything you need right here," his best friend objected.

It was Mrs. Crossopterygian who settled things, firmly and finally. "We can't afford all that time and money when summer's coming on and we have to build new mud shells! You're not going! You'll stay home and take care of the eggs!"

Maybe it is a good thing he was too dull-witted to discuss it first. After listening to all the arguments, he might have stayed home and estivated, as any good fish should.

Today, those who suggest going out into space are faced with the same arguments. "There's nothing up there to breathe. Men will have to live in pressurized suits or they may explode. What good will it do? It will cost too much when there are so many other things that need doing. And just how can we get out there at all, when there's no air to push against?"

Nevertheless, we are going out into space. Right now, the first small ships to make the trip are being built. Maybe it will take ten years, or perhaps twenty-five, to get men outside the atmosphere, but young people alive today will see it all happen.

The conquest of space has not happened yet, but it is not just science fiction now. It is not something which *may* happen, but something that *will* happen, and soon. It is as much a fact as that the Sun will shine next year.

We already have enough knowledge to tell the main facts of the adventure in space. This, then, is the story of those facts, and of what will be done with them as men go out to other worlds. It is a guidebook to the future, and the story of man's greatest exploration. To me, it is far more fascinating than any fiction can be. To me, it is a dream that has finally come true.

To the young people of today, however, it is more than a dream; it has become something they will have to know and understand, since space travel will be a real part of the world in which they are going to live.

I hope I have helped to make the learning of the facts a little easier for you—and more fun!

L. D.R.

CONTENTS

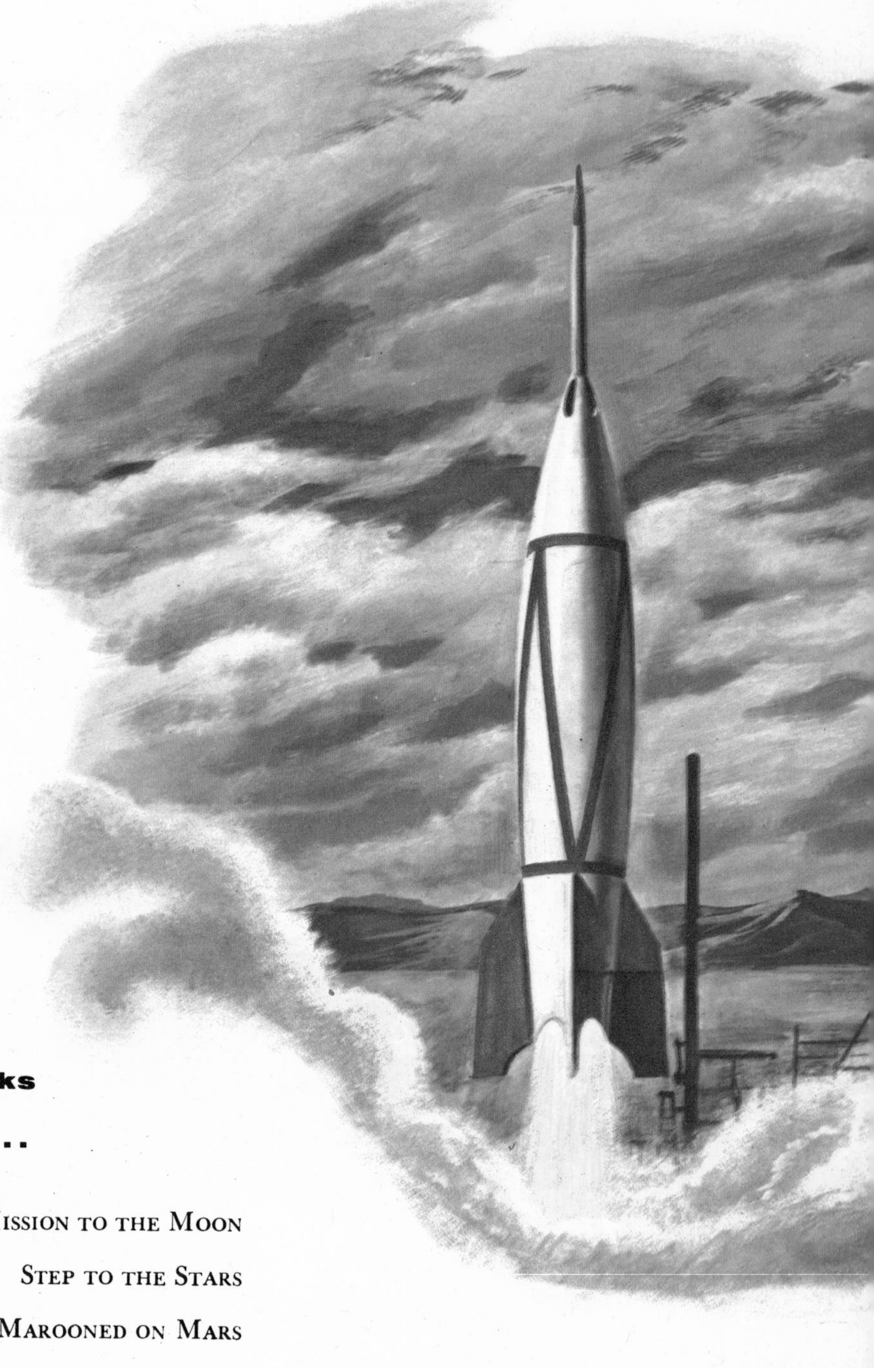

Other Space Books

by the Author...

MISSION TO THE MOON

STEP TO THE STARS

MAROONED ON MARS

ATTACK FROM ATLANTIS

SECTION I

first steps to space

JH

CHAPTER 1

how high is up?

IN ONE way, it was much easier for the first fish to move from water to air than it is for us to leave the atmosphere and get out into space. The fish had no trouble getting to the place where one left off and the other began. Water remains at about the same density from bottom to surface. Air is quite different. At sea level, 800 cubic feet of our atmosphere weighs as much as 1 cubic foot of water, which is a little over 60 pounds. A few hundred miles up, the air grows so thin that a cubic mile of it would weigh less than 1 ounce.

This makes the problem of getting out into space more difficult than almost any trip we might try after we get there.

In fact, if air behaved more like water, we would probably have space travel right now. It would not be hard to get into space then. Every square foot of the surface of Earth has a little more than a ton of air above it; but if this air were all of the same density, or thickness, as it is at the sea level, our atmosphere would reach up only about 5 miles. This would mean that the top of several mountains on Earth would actually project up into space!

Life would be a great deal different in such a world. Birds, planes and balloons could rise easily to the surface of the atmosphere; they might even leap out into space, as a flying fish leaps from the water. Men could live at the very top of the atmosphere; the temperature would drop less with height than it does now. It would be possible to dig a tunnel or build an enclosed passage to the top of Mount Everest, half a mile out in space.

Astronomers would want to work up there, where no air interfered with clear seeing. Factories might spring up above the atmosphere to produce vacuum tubes, and such things as vitamins which can be made best in a high vacuum. A *vacuum,* of course, is space with nothing in it. It would be cheaper to move the factories into empty space than to produce a good vacuum in the factories.

In such an imaginary world, spaceships might well be a reality. We would know more about space, having lived in it for years, and we could start building a space station from the top of Mount Everest. With no air to slow it down and make it fall back, the station could be built only a short distance above us.

The real atmosphere is not like that at all. It stretches up for hundreds of miles, growing thinner and thinner. At 2 miles above sea level, many people grow uncomfortable; at 3 miles up, most of us find it hard to breathe; after another mile of rising, no human beings can continue to live and work normally without extra oxygen. At 15 miles up, the best engines and superchargers we can build fail for lack of air. Yet we have not even begun to reach the end of the atmosphere.

In the Middle Ages, nobody would have been surprised that the air went higher than 200 miles. Then people who knew that the planets were millions of miles away still thought that the air stretched through all space, without any thinning out. They wrote books about getting to the Moon by tying flocks of birds together and having people carried straight up. The idea of a vacuum was something they could not imagine. They knew that air was harder to breathe at the top of their mountains, but they did not put two and two together to make four—they made it come out more like seventeen. They added many other useless ideas to the facts and talked about spirits of the air, of getting too near the fire of the Sun, and not getting enough strength through their legs because they were too far from direct contact with Earth.

The Northern Lights have been observed as high as 600 miles above the Earth's surface. Since they are caused by radiation from the Sun striking broken molecules of the atmosphere, we have to accept the fact that there is some gas at least that high. Forty years or so ago, men thought that the air came to an end at about 200 miles up, but there is too much evidence to prove this is not true.

By the time Newton discovered the law of gravitation, scientists had learned most of the basic facts and were aware that there could be no air between the planets. As late as 1800, though, people were writing stories in which balloons rose to the top of the atmosphere, or even crossed to the Moon. Still, even the scientists thought of everything in very simple terms. As they believed, the air simply got thinner as one went higher; the temperature fell steadily; and the winds became less and less.

Nothing could be further from the truth than some of those ideas. The atmosphere is so complicated and changeable that even today we are learning new and amazing things about it all the time. *Meteorologists* (men who study the weather and other things about our air) are using sounding balloons, radar and rockets to learn more. There is still much to be discovered, but the general picture is becoming clearer, though certainly no simpler. In fact, the more we find out about the atmosphere, the more puzzles and oddities there are.

The lowest layer, or *troposphere,* goes up to a height of about 8 miles. (There are no sharp divisions between layers, but heights at which certain changes become noticeable have been selected as the separations between layers.) The troposphere is the layer in which we live, about which we know most and the one easiest to understand. As we move higher in this layer, the temperature drops fairly steadily to about 70 degrees below zero, the winds increase in speed to about 80 miles an hour, and the air pressure drops without any major change in the makeup of the air itself.

Above the troposphere we find the *stratosphere,* which goes up to about 60 miles. The temperature stays about the same here until we get beyond the highest clouds, 20 miles up. Then the air begins to grow warmer again, rising to 170 degrees above zero, to change again and fall back to well below freezing at the top of this layer. The winds first decrease in speed, and then begin rising in average speed to over 100 miles an hour. Now, for the first time, we find actual changes in the air.

From roughly 15 to 30 miles above the Earth, there is a section known as the *ozone layer.* In this layer, some of the oxygen is broken apart by light from the Sun. Normal oxygen has two atoms in each molecule, which break apart to single atoms. These atoms usually get together again, but sometimes each will hastily grab onto a normal molecule, to produce one with three atoms, which is *ozone.* (Electrical discharge through the air can cause the same change, which is the reason ozone can be smelled around some big motors and generators.)

This action of the oxygen is fortunate for us. If the ozone layer were to vanish, most life on Earth would die almost at once! Ozone is transparent to normal light, but it absorbs some of the dangerous ultraviolet radiation and keeps this part from reaching us. If the ultraviolet were to reach us, it would be blinding and even fatal. However, there is no reason to worry. The more of such radiation there is, the more ozone it creates—and hence, the less of such light can get through. There is a state of perfect balance, in other words.

There are other layers within the atmosphere in which the Sun's radiation breaks up the molecules of the air. These broken parts (known as *ions,* and having an electrical charge) form what are called the *ionization layers.* Without these ions, long-distance radio would be impossible. We cannot see them, but they reflect back radio signals (except the very short radar wave lengths), instead of letting them continue in a straight line and vanish into space over the horizon.

The ions also give us the name for the next layer of atmosphere—the *ionosphere.* This layer extends from 60 to about 500 miles or more above sea level. At the bottom of the ionosphere, we have the section where meteorites, falling from outer space, become visible as they reach a depth where the air is dense enough to burn them by friction. At the top of this layer, we are practically in space.

Here the wind velocity increases steadily, up to 300 miles an hour and more. The temperature goes up even more rapidly. At about 400 miles, the thin wisp of atmosphere left is heated to as much as 4,000 degrees—far above the temperature of liquid iron!

The discovery of this heat led to many articles in the papers which claimed that space flight was now proved impossible, since nothing could stand such a temperature. Actually, it means almost nothing. The men writing the articles simply misunderstood what was meant; they were thinking of temperature as it registers on a thermometer—something one can feel. Scientists frequently have another meaning for heat; they know that heat is a good measure of how fast individual molecules of gas move about. The higher the temperature, the faster the movement of these tiny molecules (the reason why pressure goes up in a tire when it gets hot; the faster molecules strike the walls harder, increasing the pressure against them). What the scientists meant in saying the air was at 4,000 degrees was simply that the molecules were moving at as great a speed as they would if heated to such a level. It is true heat, but it will not affect a spaceship, because there are so few molecules in space at that height.

In fact, the ship might even lose heat going through this section. Each molecule that struck the ship would give up as much heat as any other molecule at such a temperature—but with such a tiny number striking the ship, the total amount of heat added would be very little. Meantime, the ship would be radiating some of its heat into space, as any warm body does. The amount of heat lost by radiation would probably be more than that gained from the air around.

Finally, above the other layers lies the *exosphere*—the outer shell. Here, scientists can detect some evidence of gas, but it is so thin that it really no longer matters. It fades out into space, but it is already so much like empty space that we might as well forget there is anything there.

The question still remains: How high is up—or how far is it to space? Truthfully, nobody can say exactly. There is no sharp line. The air begins to lose its power to resist high-speed motion at about 120 miles up; at 200 to 250 miles, rockets traveling in a circle around the Earth would be slowed only very slightly, if at all. To be on the safe side, we should say that space begins somewhere between 400 and 1,000 miles above us—and goes on and on, beyond the power of our biggest telescope to find any end.

Men have been fighting their way up through this deep blanket of air for a long time now, and have barely begun to gain any real success.

The first passenger-carrying balloon marked the beginning of man's ascent into the atmosphere. It rose in 1783 to a height of over half a mile, which was the first time men had ever gotten above the ground for any length of time without something on which to stand. The feat threw the whole world into a frenzy of excitement. Kings went up in balloons. The papers were filled with accounts of more and more flights. Stories revived the old idea of going to the Moon, even though wise men knew balloons could not rise out of the atmosphere.

In the long run, nothing came of it. The highest men ever went in a balloon was in 1935. That feat required vast sums of money for a very special type of balloon, designed to carry up men and a few instruments to study the air, as high as it

could go. It reached 72,000 feet—about 14 miles, just nicely into the stratosphere. To go higher than that would cost far more than it could ever be worth, since the lifting power of the air falls off so rapidly. A few unmanned weather balloons have gone about 5 miles higher, but that seems to be the limit.

There was new hope when the airplane was invented. A balloon depends on having a gas inside which is lighter than the air; hence, as the air grows thinner and thinner (until it weighs almost nothing), the difference in weight between the gas and the air becomes less and less. On the other hand, a plane is held up by the lift gained from its forward speed—as it goes faster, it can travel through thinner air. The answer seemed to be to build planes with greater power to go faster and climb higher and higher. Lord Dunsany wrote a story in which such a plane reached a speed high enough to leap completely out of the atmosphere and travel through space to Mars. It was a good story, but it could not happen.

The trouble is that the kind of powerful engines we know cannot be used at any great height. Normal motors and jets both depend on using oxygen from the air to burn their fuel. At a height of from 12 to 15 miles, the air becomes so thin that there is no way to draw in enough oxygen to keep those motors going efficiently. Instead of going higher than the balloon, the airplane has been forced to stop at a lower level.

There is one exception to that height limit. An experimental plane, built by Douglas Aircraft Co., and named the *Skyrocket,* has carried a passenger higher than the record set by the balloon. To do this, it had to use a rocket motor—one which needs no oxygen from the air.

This plane was designed for just one job: it was a flying laboratory to explore high-speed flight problems. It could not stay up long, since it burned its fuel at a fantastic rate. It could not even lift itself from the ground. Instead, it was carried up by a B-29 bomber, given a good speed, and then launched in full flight. Once free, it did exactly what it was meant to do. It leaped to a speed of more than 1,200 miles an hour, and its stubby wings carried it higher and higher, to a new record of just over 15 miles, probably the highest any human being has ever been.

It is possible to build rocket planes which can go higher than 15 miles, but even they have limits. After a certain height—probably around 50 miles above the Earth—the air becomes too thin for any practical wing to gain lift. Also, at the speeds needed to reach such a height, air friction begins to heat the plane too rapidly. This has become a problem with current supersonic jet planes, which require cooling to protect the pilot. At a height of 50 miles, the speed would have to be so great that the plane would literally become red-hot!

We shall have to give up the idea of gaining lift from wings and find some way to climb upward directly, using a motor that needs no oxygen from the air to burn its fuel. The only mechanism we have which fits this description is the true rocket, which rises straight up on its own exhaust, and carries both fuel and an oxidizer to burn the fuel in its tanks.

The rocket is not a very good answer. It takes tremendous amounts of fuel—expensive, highly special fuel. It cannot work efficiently at low speeds, but must rush upward as quickly as it can, much too fast for comfort. It is harder than the plane to control, and much less reliable at present. Still, it is the one means of propulsion which actually works better in a vacuum where it needs no air to support it in flight. It does not have to fight against air friction. We have to use it.

We are using the rocket, of course. We have solved most of the difficulties already. The biggest problem was how to pack enough fuel into it; that was perplexing indeed—so perplexing that a solution looked nearly hopeless 20 years ago. Today, we know enough of the answer to make flights of 100 miles up fairly routine. At least once we sent a rocket about 250 miles above the surface.

No man has yet traveled into space, but we have sent a rocket messenger ahead of us to the beginnings of true space! We are planning on sending many more shortly. After that, it will not be long before space is conquered and occupied by the human race.

CHAPTER 2

rockets and spaceships

THE idea of using rockets to get off the Earth is quite a bit older than the use of balloons. The first story to use rockets for a trip to the Moon was written more than 300 years ago, by Cyrano de Bergerac—the same man about whom the play of the same name is supposed to have been written. De Bergerac had his traveler sit in a box to which a number of skyrockets were attached.

The method was just a lucky guess, however. In those days, anything that would go up was as good a way of getting to the Moon as any other; Cyrano also used bottles filled with dew (because dew "rose" when the Sun came up). Other writers were using flocks of birds to lift their flying devices. They did not really care how it was done, since they were mostly interested in telling the readers what the Moon would be like after the travelers arrived.

In 1865, a French writer named Achille Eyraud used the idea of rocket motors in describing a trip to Venus; but this time it was not an accident. He knew there was no air between the worlds, and he gave an accurate explanation of why rockets would work. Nobody paid much attention, however; more people were reading another book by a second French writer, Jules Verne, whose *Trip Around the Moon* was also published in 1865. This story described a shell fired from a huge gun at such a speed that it could escape Earth. It would have killed anyone inside from the terrific acceleration and have burned up in the air from its speed, of course; but to most readers, at the time, it seemed more practical than rockets. Yet the idea of using rockets slowly caught on as more and more people began to realize there was no other conceivable way to get off Earth.

The rocket itself had been around for a long time before De Bergerac's story appeared. It was invented by the Chinese, probably less than a thousand years ago, and was much like a modern skyrocket. It was simply a tube, filled with solid gunpowder, having a hole in one end for the exhaust gas, and some kind of stick or tail to guide it through the air. Its first use was in war, apparently in the 13th century, where the sight and sound of such fire-breathing monsters must have frightened the enemy out of his wits.

For a long time, the rocket's chief uses were in displays for celebrations and for war, where it could start fires, act as a self-propelled shell, and carry light ropes across streams. It was used in the War of 1812, where the sight of such rockets inspired the line about "the rocket's red glare," in the anthem, *The Star-Spangled Banner,* and again in the War Between the States. Then it dropped out of use for a while, but in World War II it was back again, more useful than ever. Small rockets were fired from a *bazooka* (a portable rocket launcher) to break through tank armor, others were used against aircraft, and still others were used to get heavily loaded airplanes off the ground quickly.

Ammunition makers did a good business in such rockets, and there were long technical books on them, as well as quite a few engineers and technicians trained to make and use them. None of these people were interested in space travel. They were too busy with practical things to spend time with hopeless dreams. Besides, all their experience was with solid-powder rockets, which were not well suited for building spaceships.

The powder rocket was too hard to control. Once it was ignited, it did not stop burning until the fuel was used up, and its rate of combustion could be regulated only by the way it was built. This fact made handling a ship with such fuel very difficult. In addition, the powder fuels in general use were not good enough; the exhaust gas was too slow to drive the rocket to the speed needed, unless an impossible amount of fuel were used for the size of the ship.

Liquid fuel was the answer, since a liquid could be controlled by valves, and since a mixture of liquid oxygen and liquid hydrogen gave the hottest flame (and the highest *exhaust velocity*) then possible. Nobody, however, had any real experience with liquid-fuel rockets, and some of the problems seemed unsolvable. Both oxygen and hydrogen become liquid only at very low temperatures and extremely high pressures. They are highly explosive and hard to store, requiring strong tanks that add to the weight problem. Liquid oxygen is so corrosive that even a touch of oil in the outlet valve can explode violently when the oxygen touches it.

There were other fuels to replace the hydrogen—not as good, but still better than the solid-powder fuels. Gasoline and alcohol both were potential fuels, but there was no easy solution to the need for something to oxidize the fuel. It seemed that nothing could replace liquid oxygen; it was the only oxidizer which could be supplied in sufficient quantity to burn up the fuel at the rate needed.

Even with such fuels, the problem seemed hopeless. As early as 1920, the American Robert H. Goddard was doing some work with rockets in an attempt to find a way to explore the higher stratosphere, but nobody paid much attention. The idea of getting to space by rocket brought only amused smiles from the experts.

Then, in 1923, the whole picture changed. Nothing new was invented then; no new rocket was built; nobody found a way to do anything that could not be done before. Yet suddenly, people were forced to see that space travel was possible. All this happened because a young German professor wrote a book and paid part of the cost to have it published. After that, it was only a question of time and work before space would be conquered.

The man was named Hermann Oberth. He had never worked with rockets, and he had done no experimenting with fuels. Instead, he had simply turned to mathematics to figure out what could be done. His book, *The Rocket into Interplanetary Space,* gave the results of his figuring. It proved finally that rockets could be built to cross space to other planets, and showed how such ships could operate.

The book did something more. It created

rocket fan clubs among the readers. There were several such clubs, the most active of which was the German Rocket Society. Among the members were Oberth, Willy Ley and the young Wernher von Braun. In the end, it was because of this group that practical rockets were to be built, though it hardly seemed possible at the time.

In spite of its name, it was not a real scientific group, like the American Engineering Society, but a true fan club. The members were mostly young, and filled with plenty of enthusiasm and almost no experience. They had not done any real work with rockets of any kind. They had almost no money. To any real engineer, they must have seemed like a group of children playing with a new hobby.

Such people had made history before, however. The airplane was developed by two brothers who built bicycles for a living and flew strange kites as a hobby. The radio industry—at least the broadcasting part—was developed by a group of people who made a hobby of experimenting with Marconi's invention of the radio telegraph.

In the case of the German Rocket Society, things moved slowly at first. The group scraped together a little money and a place to work and began building rocket motors. They could not build ships until they had learned how to make an explosion chamber for the mixing of the dangerous fuel and oxygen combination. These small tubes with their fuel lines were not meant to fly; instead, they were firmly fastened down, while the amount of thrust was measured, and new designs were tried. Fortunately, in spite of accidents, no one was injured seriously.

For quite a while, all the society could do was to keep building better motors and writing up the results for other hobbyists, but they learned, little by little. Their motors burned out under the terrible heat of the explosions. Their funds were always giving out. And at times the situation looked hopeless. There seemed to be no way to build a tube that would direct the burning gas without the tube itself melting.

The society members found the answer to that. Nothing could stand the heat for any length of time, no matter how thick the rocket walls. So they made the walls thinner! Around those thin walls, they pumped the fuel before it reached the rocket explosion chamber. The fuel soaked up heat, cooling the rocket walls, and was warmed enough to fire much better. In that manner the temperature of the metal could be kept low enough so that the motors could continue working—at least most of the time.

In 1931, the first liquid-fuel rockets were actually flown. The first ones made only limited ascents, but, during the year, flights reached up over half a mile and were considered highly successful. These early rockets were still tiny things, weighing little over 10 pounds at the most. They were smaller and less spectacular than the powder rockets already in use—but they proved that liquid-fuel motors could be used. Great things were expected in the near future.

This was in Germany, however, and politics came into the scene. Hitler took over the Government, and things became very difficult. Wernher von Braun was drafted into the German Army. Later, Oberth was also drafted to work for the Government, though not much use was made of his ability. Willy Ley left Germany to go to the United States, and the rest of the group was torn with political strife and disagreements, while the Hitler Government began rounding up all the men who had been a part of the rocket society.

The fuure looked very bad for rocket work. The group had proved its idea so well that everyone now accepted rockets as a means to reach space eventually, but it seemed to be in the very far future. The American Rocket Society and the British Rocket Society were doing some work, but nothing of great importance came from their efforts, and enthusiasm cooled off as war began to threaten. It seemed that the last hope was gone when the war actually began. The powder rocket was being used for all sorts of things, but nobody seemed to have time to experiment with liquid-fuel motors.

Yet the very political troubles that had halted research now suddenly became the means for more work. Hitler was growing desperate and ready to try anything. There were men in Germany working on atomic explosives—fortunately for the Allies with no success. Everything from the pages of science fiction was thought of, and among the ideas was that of a rocket big enough to carry a bomb for hundreds of miles against England.

Now, for the first time, there was money for real research, along with laboratories, technicians and equipment. Hitler himself was interested (as he was also interested in astrology and various kinds of fortunetelling and magic). Wernher von Braun was put in charge of a secret installation at the fishing village of Peenemünde on the Baltic Sea. He had top priority and some 400 million marks to spend during the years of work.

There was no thought of better tiny rockets now. The Germans were working on the big ones. New problems came up. The biggest one, aside from the fuel (which was alcohol mixed with water to cool the motor, together with liquid oxygen to burn it), was the problem of pumping the fuel to the motor. A rocket motor burns up an incredible amount of fuel in a very short time. In a normal automobile engine, a gallon of fuel will burn for about 20 minutes at normal cruising speed; almost any pump can handle that much. In a rocket motor, as much as 50 gallons every second has to be pumped, and at high pressures, too. When one of the liquids is oxygen, the problem becomes even tougher.

The German scientists found the answer—one that would have been impossible a few years before. The pump was to be a steam-powered turbine, but with the steam developed in a new way.

Most medicine cabinets contain the chemical needed for the process. Hydrogen peroxide had been known and used for a long time, but previously, men had been forced to use only a very dilute solution of it. The medicine-chest bottle contains only 3 percent hydrogen peroxide. When the solution was made much stronger, the peroxide had a nasty habit of exploding. The compound is made by adding one atom of oxygen to a molecule of water (giving two atoms of hydrogen and two of oxygen), and it breaks down to give back the free oxygen and water, plus enough heat to turn the water into high-pressure steam.

Now, however, it was discovered that completely pure hydrogen peroxide would explode only when it touched certain substances, and that by keeping all traces of such substances out, the pure peroxide could be used. In the pump, it touched such an impurity and flashed into steam, driving the pump. The hydrogen-peroxide pump was the lightest and surest way of doing the job, and the real answer to developing big rockets.

There were plenty of lesser puzzles, but those were all solved. In 1944, after long experiments, the V-2 rockets began falling on London. The tiny rocket had grown up. It was being used in a horrible way, but that was no fault of the rocket idea, and it did not make the real progress any the less.

Over a thousand of such rockets were

fired. Carrying about a ton of payload (explosive warheads in this case), they rose to a height of 60 miles, reached a speed of 3,600 miles an hour, and traveled nearly 200 miles with their load. To do this, the actual rocket motor operated for only a little over 1 minute, with the rest of the journey continued on the speed built up! One V-2 that got out of control rose to a height of 100 miles before dropping back, far higher than anything made by man had gone before. Now the makers of the powder rockets had to admit defeat; nothing they could make would equal the liquid-fuel rocket.

Fortunately, while the rockets succeeded in working, they failed to cause as much damage as had been expected, and eventually the forces of Hitler were defeated. The Peenemünde works were captured along with a number of the rockets. The Americans brought them back to the United States, and also brought Von Braun and other scientists with them. From that time on, the work on rockets has shifted to the United States, where a huge proving-ground section was set up at White Sands, New Mexico.

Work on the rockets has not stood still in the years since the end of World War II. Much of the work is top-secret, since the rocket can still be used as a weapon, but enough information has been released to show that the real effort is being spent in trying to get out beyond the atmosphere into space. The men working on the ships are still rocket fans and men dreaming of the Moon, even though they are now scientists and engineers. Willy Ley and Dr. Wernher von Braun are still planning for the day when men can leave the Earth.

The plans and dreams have stopped being theories, and are engineering facts, needing only time and money to make them work. Already, photographs of the surface of our world from the borders of space have been made. Government contracts have been given out for the building of small ships that will reach true space, and thousands of engineers are working day and night on them.

With a somewhat better fuel combination, we could leave for space almost at once. Even with the fuels we are using now, it is just a matter of a very few years until the first journey is made. If we combine those few years of more work on the rockets with the almost certain discovery of better fuels, there is almost no limit to what we can do.

CHAPTER 3

no air to push against

WHENEVER a lecture is given on rockets, there is always one sure reaction from the audience. Sooner or later, a hand will go up and the old, old question will be asked:

"How can a rocket fly in space? There's no air up there to push against!"

When Oberth published his book, several well-known scientists made the same objection, although they should have known better. Now the scientists have admitted their error, but the question still bothers writers about space flight. In fact, one young reader of a science-fiction magazine wrote a long letter to the editor, suggesting that rockets should carry sand with them, which could be dumped into space behind them for the rocket exhaust to push against. He forgot to explain how the rocket was to carry up all that weight!

The simplest answer to this question today is the evidence: rockets work at a height where the air is too thin to matter. We have proved our theories by trying them out. We know that the air is only a nuisance to a rocket—instead of helping the flight, the air slows the rocket down by friction and has to be shoved out of the way. (In experiments, the air friction was great enough to raise the temperature of the skin of the V-2 rockets to nearly 1,200 degrees—nearly red-hot.) Still, this answer does not explain why the rocket works that way.

The real answer was given by Sir Isaac Newton 270 years ago. He stated that for every action there must be an equal and opposite reaction; that is, the same force is also exerted in the opposite direction. On Earth and in the air, this is sometimes hard to see, since we automatically brace ourselves and use friction and air resistance to soak up the "back" thrust, but we do see it work sometimes. If an ice skater pushes another skater away from him, the first skater shoots off in the opposite direction. Since the air resistance is the same on both skaters (and very slight at those speeds), this resistance obviously has nothing to do with it. We also get such a reaction when we fire a gun, since there is always a recoil.

One of the easiest ways to see this reaction is to watch a diver on a long diving board. When he leaps upward in a fancy dive, you can see the board jerk downward at exactly the same moment the diver gets his upward motion.

Superman in the comics has not learned about this reaction yet. We see pictures of him leaping a mile up into the air from the roof of a small building, or even from a window ledge. In real life, it could not happen, no matter how strong he was. The back thrust from his leap would smash the roof to splinters or rip off the whole wall holding the window. Superman would need a huge platform of thick concrete, and even that would crumble as he leaped!

In the rocket tube, the explosion of the exhaust exerts its force equally in all directions, but the sides of the rocket tube keep it from having any side thrust. Hence, it has to do its work by shoving in only two directions: backward to toss out the exhaust gas and forward to drive the rocket ahead. The air outside has nothing to do with its action. A rocket flies by the pressure of its exhaust, and nothing else matters.

Another and more difficult question is asked nowadays when a lecture is given to a group of engineers. They will admit that a rocket can move without air, but the question of how much speed it can attain concerns them. We know that to get our rocketship up to the height of 1,000 miles above Earth and keep it there, we will need to reach a speed of about 18,000 miles an hour, or 5 miles a second. Our best fuels to date, however, do not have that much exhaust velocity. *Hydrazine hydrate* (the "fuel") and *nitric acid* (which supplies the oxygen) seem to work best; yet this combination gives a top theoretical exhaust velocity of only about 2½ miles a second.

"How can a rocket go faster than its own exhaust velocity?" the engineer wants to know. "If the action you talk about is at a speed of 12,000 feet a second, how are you going to get a reaction of 26,000 feet a second?"

Whoa, now! That seems to make sense, but it does not. Put in those obvious words, it sounds impossible. The trouble here is that the words are correct enough, but something has been left out.

The real statement of rocket exhaust speeds should not be "so many feet a second," but it should be "so many feet a second *as seen from the rocket*." (In a way, this statement comes from Einstein's relativity ideas, but it is also just commonsense.) If you are on a train going at 60 miles an hour and you stand in the aisle, pushing back on a friend's shoulders, your push (or "exhaust velocity") may be only a couple of miles an hour—but he will stagger backward and you will still stagger forward. The speed of the train had nothing to do with the reaction; no matter how fast you are both traveling together, the only force comes from the thrust you give.

In the same way, no matter how fast the ship is going, the exhaust gas has the same velocity as observed from the ship, and does the same work in adding speed to that ship. Suppose the ship is going 5 miles a second and the exhaust velocity is 2 miles a second; then the exhaust gas must change from 5 miles forward to 3 miles forward per second —which is exactly the same as 2 miles a second backward.

The rule is that exhaust velocity must always be measured from the ship, not from the ground somewhere below.

Because of this rule, it is possible to drive the rocketship to a speed of two or three times the exhaust velocity of the fuel, but it takes a tremendous amount of fuel to do it. Here is where the difficulty arises in building such ships.

If all the fuel were to be burned instantly, we might expect that 1 pound of fuel would accelerate 1 pound of ship to the speed of the exhaust. In practice, that is impossible; some of the work done by the fuel is used to drive the remaining unburned fuel as well as the rest of the ship. It has been figured out that to drive a ship to exhaust velocity, if the fueled ship is to weigh 100 pounds, 63 pounds must be fuel, leaving only 37 pounds for motor, ship, cargo and everything else. To double that speed, 87 pounds of fuel are needed for each total 100 pounds; and to triple the speed, 95 pounds of each 100 must be fuel!

When we realize that the fuels in use have a practical exhaust velocity of only about 2 miles a second, and that we need a speed of more than 5 miles a second to get into an orbit 1,000 miles above the Earth, the prospect begins to look quite hopeless. It is as if an automobile had to carry more than 30 tons of gasoline at the start of each trip!

We can find ways to build the ship lighter, just as we found a way to make a lighter and better fuel pump. We have new, modern miracle metals, such as magnesium and titanium, which will give us alloys lighter than aluminum and as strong as steel. Despite new developments, no engineer today can see any way to handle 19 pounds of fuel for every pound of ship!

A better solution would be to find a fuel with a much higher exhaust velocity. Doubling the exhaust velocity would give us nearly three times as much speed and tripling it, almost seven times as much speed for the same weight!

Unfortunately, there is not much chance, from what we know now, for such greatly improved fuels. At present, we are using hydrazine hydrate as the fuel, with nitric acid as the *oxidizer* (since it contains three atoms of oxygen to each molecule, and is easy to handle). We might get more energy, if we could find a way to use fluorine-containing compounds instead of oxygen-containing compounds, and work is being done on that—but the very best theoretical fuels we could develop will only give us about twice as much exhaust velocity as what we are using now. Someday, in the far future, we may find perfect fuels that are easy to store and handle, do not need heavy tanks and have a terrific exhaust velocity. We may even find some way to use atomic energy, though all atomic power plants now are too heavy, and we have no way of making them drive spaceships yet. If we want to get into space in the near future, we shall probably have to depend on fuels much like those we are now using.

Oberth showed us how to use such fuels back in 1923, and his answer is still the best one we have.

We cannot reach the Moon or get into an orbit around the Earth, if we stick to the normal rocket we have been discussing. We can do it, however, by using the step principle—that is, making a smaller rocket ride piggyback on a larger one. We can use three such rockets, if needed.

Then the big first stage will carry us up to its top speed and be kicked away; this gets rid of all the weight of its tanks and framework, and leaves less work for the fuel of the second stage, which begins blasting at once. When the second stage has reached its top speed, it is dropped, and the final, much smaller stage, can now blast us to the speed we need. By using parachutes and letting the first and second stages fall back to the ocean, they can be recovered by ships and used again, so there will not be the waste we might expect.

We still cannot build practical ships that carry enough fuel to take off *and land* by rocket power, but we can get up into an orbit in space this way, with enough fuel left to kick us out of the orbit and make us fall back toward Earth. Then, for the first time, we can get some use out of the atmosphere. We shall put small wings on the final rocket stage and use them on the way down. Now the returning rocket can slow its fall against air resistance; it will grow red-hot for a while, but we have metals which can stand the great heat, and we can protect the pilot for the short time it will take us to lose speed and get down where the ship will begin to cool off. Then we can land just like any airplane.

Dr. Wernher von Braun has worked out a way by which such a ship can be built, using only materials and fuels we have available now. The ship is designed to carry 30 tons of freight up to an orbit (for building and supplying the permanent space station we hope to construct). The first stage of this rocket weighs about 6,000 tons, of which the fuel represents 5,000 tons, lifting the ship to 5,000 miles an hour at a height of 25 miles. Then the second stage takes over; this will weigh about 850 tons, with 750 tons of that being fuel. The rocket rises to a height of 40 miles and a speed of 14,000 miles an hour, before the second stage drops off.

The third, or final stage, complete with payload and wings, will weigh about 220 tons, with 90 tons of that for fuel, and will reach a speed of 18,000 miles an hour. It will be able to rise to its orbit 1,000 miles up and to maneuver into the proper path to keep circling the Earth forever, if that were wanted.

The whole ship, including all 3 stages, will then weigh about 7,000 tons; it will have a height of 265 feet; and its base will be 65 feet across! That is a lot of ship. Yet it is not by any means impossible. We have built many heavier ships. This weight is only about the same as that of a cruiser. There are no engineering tricks required which are beyond our ability to solve now.

The use of so much fuel is different from any other form of transportation. The first stage will be burning more than 3,000 tons of fuel per minute—50 tons a second! No other type of motor can generate even a reasonable fraction of the power for a brief time that a rocket motor can put out. Naturally, actual use of such power lasts only a brief time. Actually, the 3 sets of rocket motors have a total burning time of less

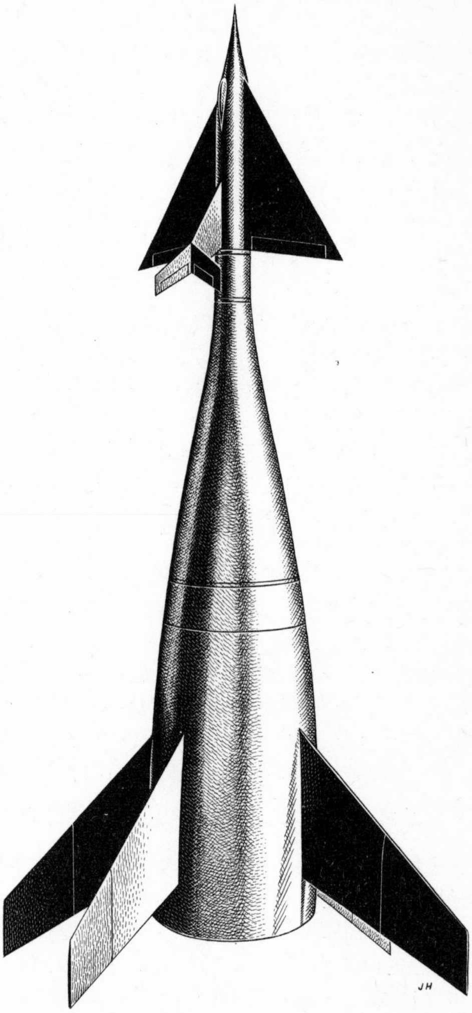

than 5 minutes altogether, and the main part of the trip up to the orbit will be made by coasting, like a shell that has left a gun.

It would be nice to burn the fuel more slowly. For one thing, the men inside the rocket are going to be crushed back into their special seats with terrible pressure from the high acceleration. But Earth's gravity and the resistance of the air both fight against the rise of the rocket, and the ship has to force its way up as rapidly as it can. It is not hard to see why this is. If the lift of the rocket motors were just enough to hold the ship up, the ship would burn fuel without going anywhere, just fighting gravity. If the lift is just twice the pull of gravity, half the work is spent in holding the ship up, but if the lift is high enough to equal four times that of gravity, then only one-quarter is wasted in fighting the pull of Earth until the ship gains speed.

Unfortunately, the faster the rocketship goes, the worse the air friction and resistance are—but, again, the sooner the ship can get above the thicker layers of air, the more efficiently the rockets can work. There is nothing a rocket engineer wants less than air to push against!

Oberth worried about air friction, too, and worked out the best way to get through the atmosphere. This path is known by the fancy term of a *synergy curve,* and is simply a proper combination of upward flight to get out of the atmosphere, followed by a turn toward the horizontal curve around the Earth that will put the ship in an orbit. Going straight up would give the maximum height, but the ship would then fall back, unless it reached enough speed to escape from Earth altogether. The first few miles of travel must be nearly straight up, until air resistance falls off. Then the ship will be turned slowly, curving gradually as it reaches thinner and thinner air, until it is rising only slightly as it moves sideways around the Earth.

There are still big problems to be solved —but the only one which will give any real trouble is that of getting enough money for the project. Securing the financial aid to carry on research has always been a dilemma for men who work with rockets, but it has been solved in one way or another in the past. Currently it appears that Government funds will cover the cost, and probably sooner than most of us think.

In 1930, the rocketship was only a dream on paper, and the boys in the first rocket fan club could only hope that sometime in the far future the problems would be solved, and such ships might be built. Now, after only a quarter of a century, a hardheaded engineer who started in that group can say flatly that it can be done in 10 years or less —and show exactly how it can be done. Since he is a scientist who has to be careful about what he says, it probably means we can build the rocketships he has designed in quite a bit less time.

Maybe, when the ships are actually circling the Earth, men will stop thinking that rockets cannot fly in space because there is no air to push against. I would like to think so, but I am not sure. There was a man in my hometown in 1930 who claimed that airplanes could not fly because they were heavier than air, and that what we saw were only pictures projected on the sky to fool people!

Most of us, however, will in all likelihood live to accept rocket flight in space just as casually as we accept flights through the air. A few of us may even be lucky enough to travel in such rockets far beyond the air, out into the depths of true space.

CHAPTER 4

operation MOUSE

WE NO LONGER have to guess when we will begin building the first spaceships, or when the first space flight will take place. The ships are being built, and they will be launched late in 1957 or early in 1958. With any luck at all, most people will be able to see them cruising above the atmosphere by that time. They will be visible with the aid of a pair of binoculars or a small telescope, and the daily papers will no doubt publish instructions on where to look for them.

This does not mean that we will have space *travel,* in the usual sense of the term. No men will be riding in these little spaceships, though a few small monkeys and mice may be sent up. Nevertheless, it will be genuine space flight, and not just a rocket shot up into the high atmosphere to fall back. Ships are being built to go up where the atmosphere is thinner than any vacuum we have been able to produce and to circle around the Earth in true orbits. They are also the first step toward the eventual construction of the bigger, man-carrying rocketships.

Strangely enough, the first word of these ships did not come from rocket experts, but from a group of *geophysicists*—men who spend their lives trying to understand more about everything connected with the Earth as a planet. The geophysicists need to know things about our world which they could not learn from the surface. They suggested that since rocket experiments were so far advanced, it would be a good idea to send up small rockets to circle Earth and send back information by radio instruments. They were particularly anxious to have this information for the celebration of the International Geophysical Year of 1957-58.

In the summer of 1955, President Eisenhower announced that the United States would co-operate, and that we would launch 10 or more such small satellites, or "birds," as some people call them. Russia also agreed to build and launch such rockets, and several other countries have joined in the program. The men working on rockets were quick to say that it was entirely possible to complete the program, known as Project Vanguard, in the time required.

The project was the first indication for many people that space flight was more than a dream, and the papers were filled with it for a few days. There was much talk about it, but surprisingly little objection. Congress met with engineers to find what could be done, and then agreed to provide the money.

The situation was much different from the development of the first real rocket, the V-2. That missile was built for war and death, in absolute secrecy. Project Vanguard is a peaceful undertaking, to be carried out by international co-operation and with the full consent of everyone.

Contracts for building the "birds" have been given to several manufacturers. The Glenn L. Martin Company is building them for the United States Navy, and probably hundreds of companies throughout the country are making parts and materials, while laboratories are working overtime to find better fuels. The launching can be done with hydrazine and nitric acid, but we naturally want the best fuel we can find, since that will make the whole operation easier.

A code name had to be found for the little spaceship we are building. Official language cannot just call them little ships, or even "birds." That would not be official-sounding enough. Yet nobody wants to walk around talking about Unmanned Orbital Stations of Minimum Size for Exploration of the Upper Atmosphere and Space! Somebody had to find a title that could be abbreviated, and a name was coined finally that seemed to do the trick.

The little spaceship will be known as Minimum Orbital Unmanned Satellite of Earth—and the initials of that title are MOUSE. So we can call the program Operation MOUSE. It will be only an accident if we use mice in the ships—the name will not refer to them, however.

No exact details have been given out yet, but enough has been said by the experts to give us a fairly clear idea of what the

MOUSE will be like and how it will be launched.

This MOUSE will be about the size of a basketball. It will be shaped something like an ice-cream cone with the end sealed shut—since it will be the tip of a two-stage or three-stage rocket, that is a logical shape. Outside, it will be painted to reflect the maximum amount of light, to make spotting it easy. Inside, it will be packed with all the equipment possible to cram into it.

There will be a battery inside, to operate the scientific instruments and to power the tiny radio transmitters that will send back signals which will let receivers below know what the instruments read. Such instruments and transmitters—known as *telemetering devices*—are already used in weather balloons and rockets, so nothing new has to be invented, though work will be done in perfecting even lighter instruments and better transmitters. These will probably use transistors instead of tubes, since very little power is needed to operate them.

The miniature spaceship will probably be launched from three-stage rockets, which will look something like V-2 or Viking rockets, each with a smaller rocket fastened to its nose, and the MOUSE located at the nose of the small rocket. The first stage will take it up part way, then drop free; the second will drive it to its speed of about 18,000 miles an hour, and then will drop free, too; and finally, a small charge will set the MOUSE into a circular orbit around the Earth.

The orbit will be at a height of about 300 miles, where the little object will circle the world below once each 90 minutes. At this distance from the surface, there is considerable doubt whether there is enough atmosphere to make the little satellite fall back from loss of speed. The air friction can almost be forgotten, and a nearly permanent orbit could be expected.

However, it is not planned that MOUSE will stay up forever. The circular path, in all probability, will not be completely accurate, since controlling it from the ground with the simple maneuvering devices will not permit perfection. It will dip closer to Earth in part of its orbit, and retreat farther in other parts. A number of factors make the scientists believe that it will eventually lose speed and begin to fall back toward Earth. Then, when it hits denser atmosphere at its falling speed, friction from the air will make it burn to a fine dust, just as meteorites do. In the meantime, though, the instruments will have sent back all their valuable information.

The cost of Project Vanguard is estimated at between 10 and 20 million dollars.

This cost is sufficient proof of how wrong many of the old science-fiction stories were. In them, it was common for some scientist to figure out a new type of rocket and then build a ship in his own workshop, after which he went sailing out to the planets. When one realizes that even a tiny ship is going to cost millions, and will require thousands of men and hundreds of scientists, it begins to seem that space flight must be undertaken by the governments or by very large business concerns. No individual can get into space by himself.

The cost, incidentally, will include an allowance for the fact that some of the ships will fail. There will have to be enough ships in spite of some failures to get the 10 we expect to launch into their orbits. From those failures, we shall learn what to avoid in our future work.

The expense is not too much for what we hope to learn, either. Aside from the experience with handling space rockets, we shall be able to answer hundreds of questions science needs to have answered. We shall learn exactly how dense the upper atmosphere is; so far, we have been forced to calculate this from other things we can observe. With a true answer to the density, we can check on those observations and in turn use them to give us better answers to other things.

We shall even be able to tell the exact shape of the Earth. We know it is flattened at the poles and bulges at the equator, but we need a better check on this matter.

There is quite a bit of information which our astronomers need, which the satellite can supply. Meteorologists need other facts, some of which will help them in their efforts to get better long-range weather predictions.

We are also very much interested in knowing more about the radiation that strikes Earth from the Sun and from other sections of space. The Sun sends out all kinds of radiation, not just light rays. There are ultraviolet rays, radio waves, and even X-rays. Many of these do not get through the atmosphere in sufficient amounts to matter, but we need to know more about them. There are also the mysterious *cosmic rays* which seem to come out of space from all directions. We can detect them on Earth, but as these rays pass through the atmosphere, changes are produced which make them harder to study. Since they are the form of radiation with the most energy, a better understanding of them will be valuable in many fields, including atomic physics.

Best of all, for those interested in rocketships, we shall learn a great deal more about what our first explorers in space will have to face. Those cosmic rays may prove dangerous to men, in which case our ships will have to be much heavier than we think, to offer protection. We shall also have our first chance to study the effects of a lack of weight. (While in an orbit, there would be no feeling of weight inside the satellites.) So far, we have never been able to study weightlessness for more than a very short time; but with small animals in one or more of the satellites, we can telemeter back enough information to tell whether lack of weight will be a serious danger to men in space. In this way, the unmanned satellites will pave the way for manned ships to follow.

When the announcement of Project Vanguard was made, many people thought at first that it might mean we were giving up our hope of sending up manned ships and building manned stations in space. Nothing could be further from the truth. MOUSE is not meant to replace the idea of the true station in space, but will simply make it easier for us to do the work needed to get such a full-sized satellite up.

The experts who have worked this all out never expected to get into space in one jump. Many writers and fans who did not fully realize the problem had a picture of someone building a ship here and taking off straight for the Moon, in the very first attempt. By now, we know this would not work very well. We have been getting closer and closer to the way Oberth and the men of the German Rocket Society expected it to be, even from the beginning of their research.

We have found that we must move in slow steps. It is as if we had an enormously deep and dark cave into the Earth which had to be explored. One way would be to get together a group with ropes and have them start down—but they might not come back. There might be gas or other dangers there about which they did not know. The scientific way would be to lower instruments and cameras first, to find out what the cave was like. Then a few men would be sent down to probe the way. Only after the most careful study could a full exploration be made; it would succeed, though, because it would be properly equipped and its members would be fully aware of what was needed and what to expect.

In the long run, such a careful method would be both cheaper and faster. The same applies to our step-by-step method of getting out into space.

(Let us suppose that our fish named Crossopterygian did come up out of the water onto dry land. He would have had to learn to gulp air from the surface while he stayed in water, and developed his air bladder into a kind of lung. Then he would have come out for a little while, and his remote descendants would have stayed out longer and longer, until one could finally live on land.)

Almost nothing that goes into making MOUSE will be usable directly on the men into space. The fuels used and research on new fuels should result in better rockets. The rocket motors on the ships that lift MOUSE will be usable directly on the stages of the man-carrying rockets.

Of course, the ships used in Operation MOUSE will be much smaller than will be needed to carry men up, but the motors will not necessarily be any different, even in size. The real spaceships will not use just a single motor. It would be too big to be practical. (Remember that it would have to use tons of fuel every second!)

Instead, the three-stage ships needed later to carry men will have many small motors mounted together in each stage. In the design suggested by Dr. von Braun, 51 such motors would be used in the first stage, 22 in the second, and 4 in the final stage—a total of 77 motors.

We would have to build and try out such motors experimentally in any event. The only way to try them would be to use them to drive smaller ships, and that is exactly what we are doing in putting MOUSE into its orbit. Hence, we are not even being delayed by the work on this project. While we are getting the little satellites up, we are going ahead full steam on the building of the motors for the next step. We are designing the motors, and also developing the machinery and factory equipment needed to build them. Almost every cent spent on Project Vanguard is going to be that much less we shall have to spend on getting the bigger rockets into production.

We are losing nothing, and we are gaining a great deal.

Also, we are making it much more likely that we will go ahead with the development of space travel. At present, most of the development of the big ships is only in the form of plans on paper. It is difficult to convince anyone that it is worthwhile to devote time and money toward the converting of plans into fact. Once we have the rocket motors already designed and proved, and once we can point up to MOUSE over our heads to show that it can be done, everything will be much easier. With this step taken, the next step will seem much more logical.

In a way, the various stages leading to the development of the spaceship are similar to those of the airplane. Many people had designed airships on paper and had worked out the basic theory of air flight. There was considerable difficulty in building a machine that would actually work, however. The Wright brothers did not try to construct man-carrying ships at first. They studied all the theory they could find, and then began flying kites on strings, to study the actual behavior of such ships. They found ways to overcome the difficulties by trying out their theories on such kites. When they finally built an airplane that was supposed to fly with a man aboard, it flew.

MOUSE, then, is the kite we are using to test and design our true, full-sized spaceship. Once we have the tiny satellites up, the time for true flight into space by men will have been shortened to a very few years.

SECTION II

the exploration of space

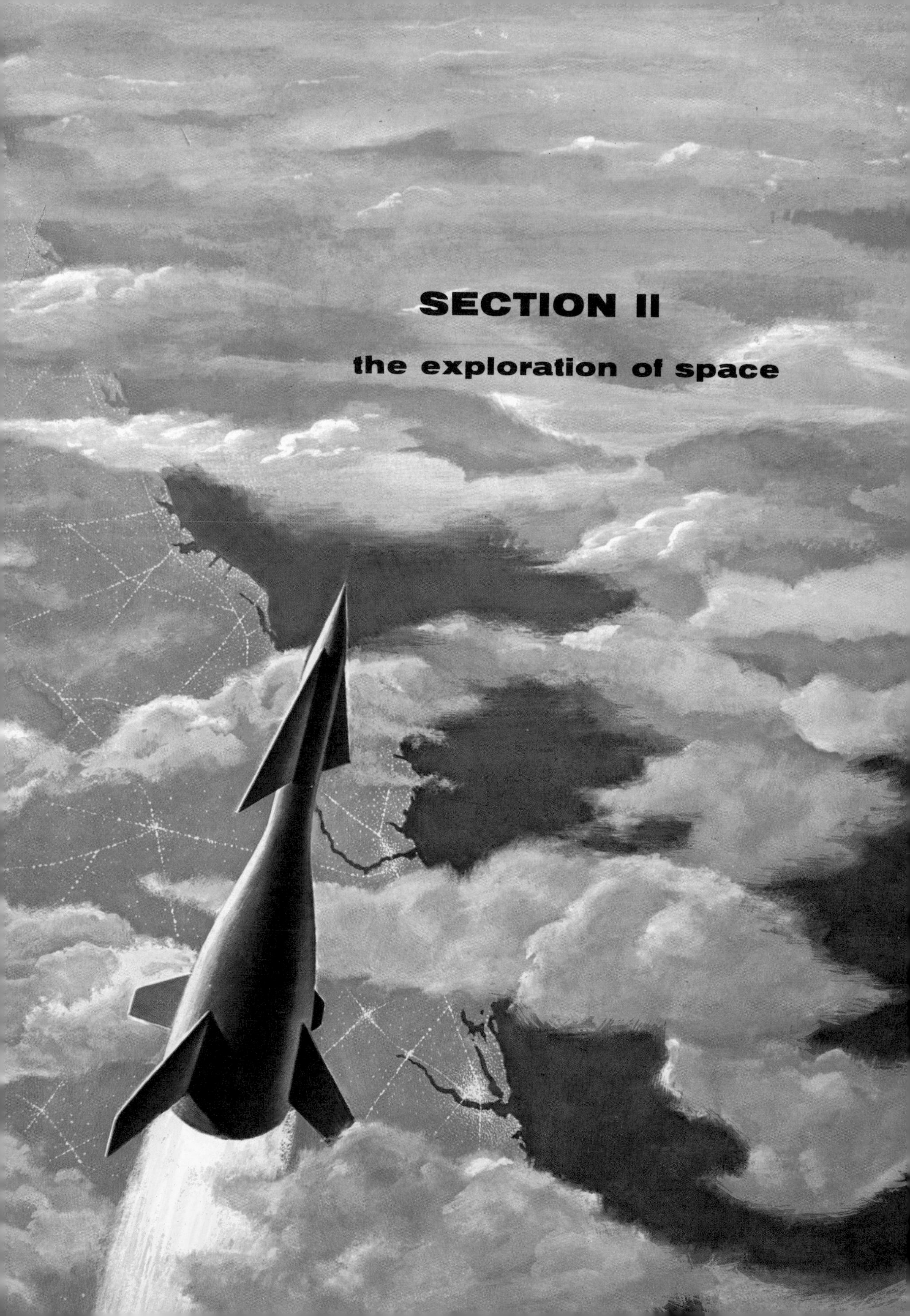

JH

CHAPTER 5

the endless ocean

THERE is a saying among scientists and engineers that nothing at all is harder to make than nothing at all.

On Earth, this is certainly true enough in two different fields. It is not only hard—it is impossible—here to make space which contains nothing at all; nobody has yet succeeded in making as good a vacuum as can be found a few hundred miles above the surface of the Earth.

The same rule applies to temperature, too. Zero on the scientific (centigrade) thermometer is the place where water freezes; but this is still quite warm, in some ways. *Absolute zero*—the complete absence of any heat—is located between 200 and 300 degrees lower than this! Since heat represents the movement of molecules (properly in a gas, though some movement occurs in solids, too), absolute zero would be the point at which molecules would come to a complete rest. Thus far nobody has been able to get all the heat out of anything. Science has gone down very close to the absolute limit, but up to now it has not been reached.

There was another saying, which was believed by even educated men for a long time, that Nature abhors a vacuum. They had reason to think so, since the air always rushed so rapidly into anything resembling a vacuum. The reason was not Nature's dislike of a vacuum, but simply the fact that air is under pressure from the air above it, and that pressure of 15 pounds every square inch tried to force the air into anything at a lower pressure.

In any event, both of these sayings are exactly wrong when we get into space.

Rather than avoiding a vacuum, Nature seems to have filled most of the Universe with just that. The planet Pluto lies billions of miles beyond the Sun; yet if all the matter in space, including planets, from the Sun to Pluto in all directions, were collected together on the surface of the Sun, it would not increase the size of the Sun enough to amount to anything! Billions multiplied by billions and again multiplied by billions of cubic miles of that space are nothing but a better vacuum than any we can make. The Sun and all the planets are only tiny lumps in that vast area of emptiness.

When we get beyond Pluto, space is even emptier. We live in a "thick" section of space. Beyond Pluto lie so many millions of millions of miles of space that light has to travel for years to get from the nearest star to us. Stretching out from star to star is the Milky Way, the galaxy of stars in which the Sun lies. When the Milky Way ends, there are unthinkable distances that reach to other galaxies of stars. The Universe goes on and on, piling emptiness on emptiness, until even our greatest telescopes cannot see the end. We do not even know whether there is an end, or what such an end could be like.

Space is an endless ocean, so far as we can learn, with all the stars we can see in it taking up only the tiniest fraction of the territory it covers.

We can forget about the whole Universe for the time being, however, and consider the territory from a few hundred miles above Earth out to the Moon and the planets. (Certainly in our lifetime we will not get any farther than the planets!) This section of space is much less empty than that between the stars, but it is still empty beyond any meaning we have for the word now.

If all the matter in the typical cubic mile of space between the Moon and the Earth could be compressed into a pellet, you could have it in one of your pockets and never know it was there. This matter exists now as a few molecules spread out at great distances, with an occasional tiny speck of dust here and there, at even greater distances.

If we took up a vacuum tube with us into the space a thousand miles above Earth and broke it open, gas would rush *out* of it into the thinner space around! Up there, creating a good vacuum would be no problem at all.

Getting an extremely low temperature would also be easy. Scientists talk about the temperature of space, because the few molecules of gas there have motion and can thus be called "hot," but there may be degrees without much "quantity" of heat. The same can be true of electricity. *Volts* refer to the level or degree of energy in electricity; quantity is measured in *amperes.* If you have electricity at even millions of volts with a small enough fraction of an ampere, it cannot hurt you—though even a hundred volts at several amperes can possibly kill you. A static machine or spark coil can make high-voltage and low-amperage current, and many people have felt the shock from such a source without harm.

In space, there are so few molecules around that the temperature of them has almost no effect at all. We can think of space itself as having no temperature. It will not be quite accurate scientifically, but such an idea is fairly correct. The only temperature effects will be from radiation.

Anything in space will be heated by the radiation from the Sun—the radiation is much stronger with no air to cut it down. Any object out in space will give off its own heat and grow colder wherever the sunlight does not fall. A spaceship, for instance, will grow hotter on the side facing the Sun and will lose heat on the side in the shadow.

Thus, if we want very low temperatures—even ones close to absolute zero—we can get them by putting something out in space where no sunlight can fall on it. Or we can get very high temperatures by arranging mirrors so that the sunlight is concentrated on all sides.

There is another way we can juggle the heat to suit ourselves. Remember that space is a vacuum, and that such a vacuum is a very good insulator of heat, as is shown by the vacuum bottles used to keep liquids hot and cold. Heat can only be gained or lost through radiation. On Earth, most heat is gained by what is known as *convection*—the passing of heat from one object to another. Thus, the air around a steam "radiator" (which should be called a *convector*) picks up the heat from the hot metal and carries it to us, where our bodies pick it up from the air. In space, we have nothing to transfer the heat in this way outside the walls of a spaceship.

We can, on the other hand, do things to

change the amount of heat we obtain by radiation, or the amount we give off in the same manner. Anything that is white or silvery bounces back most of the radiation it receives; anything a dull-black color soaks up most of the radiation. We know this already, which is the reason people in hot countries wear white hats against the Sun.

So by having panels in our spaceship that are silvery on one side and black on the other, we can regulate the temperature just by turning the right number of panels over.

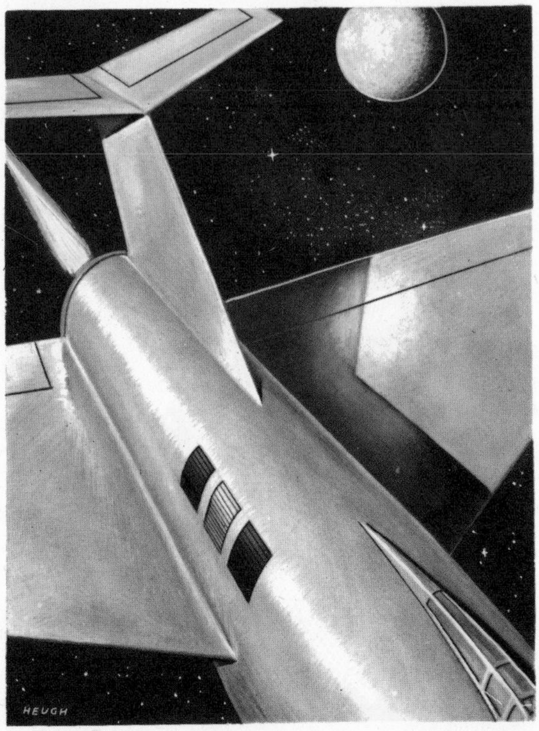

This fact brings up another point. We have been talking about space being empty, but this applies only to matter. There is almost no matter in most of space, but it is anything but empty of other things. It is busy and bustling, with torrents of energy in various forms pouring through it in all directions.

The Sun is sending out a whole group of radiations, beginning with radio frequencies, moving up in frequency through light rays, and right on until we find even X-rays being sent out. (Fortunately the X-rays are in much smaller quantities than light, so that we will not have too much trouble protecting ourselves from such radiation.) Other radiation is coming from the stars, though in lesser quantity. Even the planet Jupiter is filling the *ether* (as space is sometimes called) with certain radio frequencies.

Those frequencies are strong enough to be detected now on Earth, through all the resistance of our blanket of air. While they are true radio signals, they are not a sign that there is intelligence on Jupiter. Scientists can tell the difference between messages that have meaning and any kind of natural, meaningless radiation—even though they could probably not decode such messages, if there were any. The signals from Jupiter have no sign of intelligence in them, but must be caused by some natural action going on there.

Cosmic radiation is pouring through space, too; nobody is sure of what causes that yet, but we know it is there.

Then there is gravity. About this we know even less. We know the rules that matter obeys when pulled by gravity, but almost nothing about what gravity is. The Earth's gravity grows weaker as we move out from the surface, and we can figure out how strong it will be. The rule is that gravity decreases with the square of the distance from the center of Earth. This means that if we go out 4,000 miles into space, we are twice as far from the center of Earth. So we square 2—multiply it by itself—to get 4, and divide the gravity pull by that figure, leaving us with only $\frac{1}{4}$ normal weight. At 36,000 miles distance, we are 10 times as far from Earth's center, so we weigh only 1/100 as much as we do on our planet. From then on, we keep growing lighter and lighter, but never quite lose all our weight, unless we reach a place where the pull of something else (such as the Moon) exactly equals that of Earth.

It is also not quite accurate to state that all the space between the planets and moons is empty. Most of it is so empty that we can forget about the few molecules there, or the little motes of dust. There are, nevertheless, a few objects traveling in even this empty space that we cannot overlook.

These bodies are the *meteorites.* Most people who have seen science-fiction movies or read stories about travel in space already know about them. In fact, according to some of the stories, it might almost seem that a ship could hardly get out of the atmosphere before being hit and battered by such meteorites. Happily, the situation is not nearly that bad.

It is true that millions of these meteorites strike the atmosphere of Earth every day. It is also true that these bits of stone or iron travel through space at speeds as high as 25 miles a second. This does not mean that a spaceship will be in constant danger from them.

In the first place, Earth is much larger than any spaceship we can ever build. It presents a target to the meteorites of close to 100 million square miles, and our spaceship will have an area of only a small fraction of 1 square mile to be hit. That reduces the number of hits by a proportion of a billion to one, or more!

In the second place, most of the meteorites that hit are too small to matter much. Most of them are tiny bits, no bigger than the particles of dust that float in the air. They may strike with tremendous energy for their size, since their speed is so high, but even the thin skin of the rocket would stop them without any serious damage. (Also, remember that these particles will often be going around the Sun in the same direction as Earth, which itself is traveling at 18 miles a second; hence the difference in speed between the meteorites and a rocket near Earth will not be so great as it seems.)

Suppose we consider meteorites the size of the periods on this page. Then the number of these bodies has decreased considerably. Now we are not in such trouble, after all. It has been figured out that for each thousand square feet of surface, the spaceship circling around the Earth could stay up about 4 years for every time it would be hit by such a particle.

Thus with even a large rocketship, the chances are that meteorites the size of a period would not hit more than once a month—and probably would do no serious damage, or even puncture the outer plating of the rocket.

When we consider meteorites the size of a large pea, they become so rare that the rocketship might stay up for thousands of years without being hit by one.

There are a few truly big meteorites in space. Once in a while, one large enough to fall through all the layers of atmosphere without burning up will strike Earth. There have even been a few which weighed tons after they landed, but these are unusually huge ones, and very rare. It has been estimated that a rocket traveling between the Earth and the Moon could make 4,000 such trips before it would have much chance of being hit by a meteorite large enough to do any real damage.

I am afraid that science-fiction writers have exaggerated in the matter of this danger. You cannot blame them, since it *could* happen, and since it makes for greater interest in many of the stories. Still, when you read accounts of huge meteorite swarms, with great rocks moving through space, you can assume that somebody was stretching the facts for a good story.

There may be swarms of meteorites—in fact, we know there are, since some of these swarms hit the Earth every year. Most of the meteorites, though, are tiny specks, and even then these are great distances apart. One the size of a baseball would be so rare that it would be a remarkable accident if our spaceship ever came near it—and then it would undoubtedly be detectable by radar, so that we might have warning in time.

Even if one of the larger, pea-sized meteorites hit the ship, the damage could usually be repaired. At the speed of its hit, the meteorite would turn boiling hot—boiling for rock, not for water—and might drive quite a hole through the skin of the ship. Unless it actually hit some vital piece of machinery, the ship could be patched against air loss without too much danger.

Our spaceship would be safer in this regard than almost anything we know. Even walking along a quiet country road in daylight is much more dangerous than traveling in a spaceship through a swarm of meteorites!

Also, in spite of some stories in films, there would be no sound of meteorites going past the spaceship. Sound is made up of pressure changes in air which are taking place very rapidly. Since there is no air in space, there could be no sound. We could hear a hit through the walls and the air inside the ship, but unless a meteorite did hit the ship, there would be only complete silence as it went by.

In fact, a man in a spacesuit would be totally unable to talk to anyone else in space, unless he had a radio or were actually touching the other person. Sound will carry through anything solid. The man could touch helmets with another to talk, or even send his voice along a tight wire from suit to suit, but even a paper-thin layer of vacuum is enough to cut off all sound.

Maybe we should stop calling it the empty vacuum of space and call it the silent one!

CHAPTER 6

survival in space

SOMETIME ago, an important meeting was held on space travel, at which expert after expert told of the progress his group was making. One by one, the questions and problems of flight through space were asked and answered. Everything began to look better and better, until finally one man rose from the audience and asked the question that everyone had avoided.

"All right. You can build ships to fly in space," he said. Then he shook his head. "But can you build pilots to fly them?"

That was a question that had been a worry for a long time—as the question of the human factor has always worried engineers. It applies to many things. Cars, for instance, could be built to go at 200 miles an hour on the highway. So far, nobody has figured out a way to build the right kind of people to drive them at that speed!

Now we know we can get ships out into space. There are still many questions that need answers before we can be sure of man's ability to survive in space, once he gets there. While it will be nice to get our ships out of the atmosphere, the real dream has always been to have people aboard those ships.

Considerable work has been done in trying to find the answers, but nobody can be sure of everything yet. The Air Force has a Department of Space Medicine in which men are put through the closest imitation of space conditions that can be made. There is no way yet of approximating actual conditions. There will not be, until we can send men up in ships to face the real thing.

One of the biggest problems is the lack of weight after men reach the orbit. In such an orbit, the pull of gravity is balanced by the outward pressure of *centrifugal force* from the rapid circling of the planet below. (The same centrifugal force is what will hold a weight at the end of a string when it is rapidly twirled in a circle.) There is no feeling of weight under such conditions.

The sensation is not exactly the same as floating in water. There, even with the temperature the same as the body and without the feeling of wetness, only a little of weightlessness can be imitated. True, the body is balanced exactly against its weight by the surrounding water; but the inner organs of the body and the delicate balance organs in the ear can still feel a downward pull. In space, there would be no pull at all, once the rocket went into its orbit around the Earth.

It is hard to imagine living without an "up" or "down." Hot air could not rise by itself, since the word "rise" applies only when there is an "up." Hair and clothing would not stay down. Anything not fastened in place would be free to float about. A match would not stay lighted, unless moved about or in a current of air from a fan, since it would use up all the oxygen around it, and no new air would flow in—the hot air would not move away to let the fresh air arrive!

Liquids would not stay in a container. If you look at water in a narrow tube, you will see that it curves in the center; small quantities of water will collect into tiny balls, even against gravity. There is a tension at the surface which tries to make the liquid form a shape with the smallest amount of surface for the amount of liquid—and a sphere fits such requirements. So all liquids would clump into spheres, if permitted.

A steak could not be fried without some type of clamp to hold it against the pan. Otherwise, the heating of the surface would produce tiny jets of steam from the water present in all meat, and the steam pressure would toss the steak out of the pan immediately. Even in a broiler, it would jump around violently unless fastened in place.

There are solutions to most of the drawbacks of lack of weight. Liquids could be kept in sealed containers, something like the plastic bottles in which ketchup and mustard are now being sold. A self-sealing nipple could be provided so that a man could drink by putting it in his mouth and squeezing the bottle. Bathing would be a problem, but it could be accomplished by using carefully dampened sponges. It would have to be done inside some type of plastic bag or else in a strong stream of air, to keep drops of water from floating around, but it could be managed.

Tools would probably be magnetized—including eating utensils—so that they would stay in place when set on a metal section. Most other articles could be fastened permanently in place. Cords strung along the walls—and here, every wall is the same, since there would be no true ceiling or floor—would provide handholds for moving about, or men could wear magnets in their boots and walk on any section containing iron.

There is nothing that can be done about man himself. He cannot make any radical changes in his own body. It is a wonderful body in many ways, capable of adapting to conditions that vary from the tropics to the poles, beyond the range of any other animal. It has already permitted us to do things that would have seemed unbelievable to our ancestors, but there must be limits to how much it can adapt. The question is whether those limits are reached too quickly for men to endure life in space.

Men, after all, are adapted for living in a condition of weight.

Fortunately, most of the problems can be met by our bodies. We can swallow without gravity, though some animals cannot. We can even swallow when upside down. Our blood circulates evenly, no matter whether we stand on our heads or our feet; automatic changes take place to adjust the body.

Whether we can go on for days and weeks without gravity is another matter, and nobody can answer that yet. The best indications we can find are that we can adapt, but we cannot be sure.

The chief question is whether we can adjust our senses to the new conditions. We are so used to having a feeling of down that most of our movements and ways of thinking are based on it. We do not think about balance when we walk—we simply move. In space, though, every movement must be deliberate and carefully planned, at least until new habits are learned.

Also, we have a small organ in our ears that is meant to tell us just where up and down are. The semicircular canals are tiny coiled tubes, partly filled with liquid which flows to their lowest section, where little hairlike nerves sense it. If we are spun about too quickly, centrifugal force throws the liquid out of position, and we get dizzy. In the absence of gravity, the liquid in the tubes would not behave properly at all. We might find ourselves permanently dizzy, with the sickness in our stomachs turning into convulsions that would make survival impossible. With our sense of orientation, or our feeling of location with respect to our surroundings, completely out of order, we might not be able to perform the normal movements of our bodies nor undertake the necessary operations of the instruments with only our sense of sight to guide us.

However, the evidence is not quite so hopeless as that. There may be many who cannot adapt, but apparently some people can. Ballet dancers spin in a tight circle, but they do it without becoming ill by snapping their heads to control the fluids in the ear canals. However, some people seem to be able to spin without such tricks, and to learn to overcome any feeling of dizziness and feel no discomfort.

There are also signs that we can learn to get along without a sense of up or down, since many pilots in the early planes reported going through overcast to find themselves flying upside down without realizing it. (This was before we had instruments to tell them where down was.) Apparently to men, the sense of orientation is less necessary than the information from our eyes. If that is true, we should be able to find enough spacemen without too much trouble.

We have had some experience with a seeming lack of gravity. The pilot of a rocket-propelled airplane stayed in a dive where there was no feeling of weight for almost a minute, and reported no bad results. We also sent up mice in one of the V-2 rockets and kept cameras working to record their reactions. The films show the small animals floating about without weight, but with no ill effects that we could determine.

For a time, there was also some question as to whether we could stand the feeling of too much weight during takeoff. Rocketships must take off and gain speed very rapidly, and the acceleration can thrust the pilot backward (as a sudden acceleration throws the driver back against the seat of a car) with a force several times as great as our normal weight.

The answers to the question of too much weight have been found. Men have been spun at the end of a beam until centrifugal force pressed them outward as strongly as six times the pull of gravity. At that pressure, they seem to weigh six times as much as they usually do. Their flesh is pulled back savagely; pictures show terrible grimaces. Their arms become too heavy to lift, and breathing becomes extremely labored. The men withstood the pressure for longer periods than the rockets will need to accelerate, and they came out of the test with no damage done. They bore the pressure in a sitting position; when lying flat against the force, they could take it much better. All rocketships will be equipped so that their crews can lie prone during takeoff. Automatic pilots will guide the ships up, but in an emergency, the men aboard will be able to endure the acceleration well enough from a prone position to handle the controls.

Plenty of minor troubles relating to space travel have been studied—minor only because we were sure the answers could be found. The proper mixture to be used as air in the ships and stations has been considered, for instance. The normal air could be used in both, but it would not be the most economical answer in terms of weight. Our air has about four parts of nitrogen for one

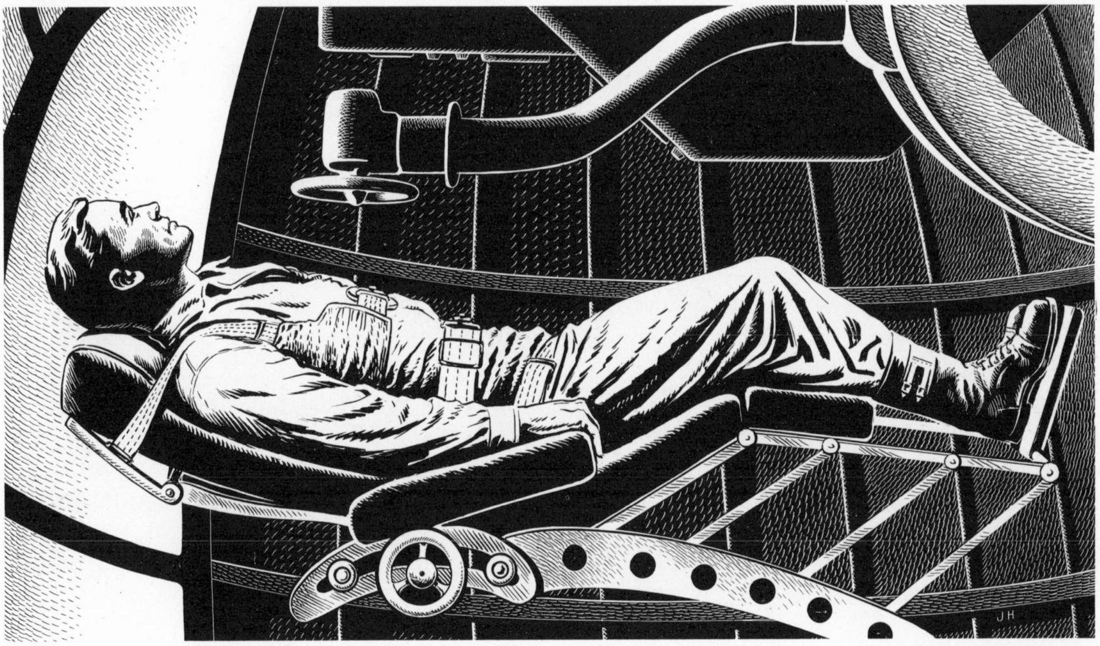

of oxygen, the latter being the gas we need. If pure oxygen could be used, it would save most of the weight (and the extra weight of tanks to hold the reserve nitrogen).

Pure oxygen at our normal 15 pounds per square inch of pressure would be too active. Men would have what is known as an *oxygen jag*—that is, the excess of oxygen would ruin their judgment and overstimulate them until they were completely unable to do their work properly. One proposal has been to use helium in the air instead of nitrogen—at a considerable saving of weight, since helium is the second lightest gas known. (Hydrogen, the lightest, is too combustible to be safe.) The use of helium would have the further advantage that men would be less apt to get the *bends*—a painful condition caused by the forming of bubbles of nitrogen in the body when the air pressure suddenly drops, as it might in case of a leak or puncture in the ship.

Another solution would be to use pure oxygen, but to cut the pressure down to about 3 pounds—the amount of pressure in the atmosphere caused by oxygen. This would provide people with the same amount of oxygen with each breath, but add nothing to the weight absolutely necessary. In addition, this low pressure would be even more protection in case of a leak, since the body would be adjusted to much less outside pressure. There are problems involved, though; the sound of the human voice is adapted to our full pressure, and it would change under less; at 3 pounds it might be hard to carry on normal conversations. We also do not yet know how well such an atmosphere of pure oxygen at lower pressure would work. Maybe some combination of the last two ideas might prove best. Whatever the answer, it can be solved right here on Earth, in pressure tanks, before any flight is attempted, and research on such a project is being done already.

The biggest remaining problem, other

than lack of gravity, is the uncertainty about the effects that radiation above the atmosphere may have on people.

Our air cuts off a great amount of radiation coming from the Sun and space which might be harmful. The ozone layer cuts down the amount of ultraviolet light we get, for instance. When we go into space, we can cut off such harmful radiation easily enough, since the walls of the ship will stop all light, and since even ordinary glass will hold back most of the ultraviolet. There are other forms of radiation, though.

We do not know yet the extent of harmful radiation in space. The body can stand a certain low amount of X-rays; and at present it seems as if there may not be too much of them in space, even though the Sun does send out some. Also, in the X-ray range, some radiation is harder to screen out than others, and the lower the energy level, the easier the radiation will be to handle.

This problem may not prove too perplexing. At any event, metal makes a fairly good screen for the average X-rays, as can be seen by the fact that any piece of metal will show up strongly in a fluoroscope—more strongly than the bones, usually. This is because metal is much less transparent to X-rays than we are. The ship will have a skin of metal around it, which should take care of most of this danger.

Cosmic rays are another cause for concern. We know that less of these reach the surface of the Earth than will be found in space. So far, we have only been able to estimate roughly the amount we would find beyond the atmosphere. These radiations are much more penetrating than X-rays. Cosmic rays have been detected through many feet of solid lead, though much less strongly than above such a shield. Cutting them off completely is much too difficult a job for any kind of shielding we could put around a spaceship.

We cannot be sure of the amount of danger from radiation until we get full reports from Project Vanguard, after the little satellites send back cosmic-ray counts from above the air.

The prospect looks hopeful. The air is not by any means a perfect insulator against cosmic radiation. A large part of that radiation must be striking us now; Geiger counters show us that these cosmic rays are bombarding us all the time. However, while this bombardment may cause some damage to our cells, it is not so great that the body is seriously harmed by it. We do not usually think about it, and the cells replace or heal themselves pretty well.

The increase in cosmic radiation above the atmosphere may cause slightly more harm to the bodies of the men in spaceships, but there is a good chance that it will still be within safe limits. As long as it is not above a certain level, radiation—even atomic radiation—can be withstood by the body, without that body even being aware of damage.

Like the information on living without weight, the effects of cosmic radiation must wait for a sure answer. To the best of our knowledge, men can live in space. Some men will be able to stand it better than others. Trained men, who go up first for short trips to test the rockets, will certainly be able to stand more than untrained men. So by selecting the best men for the job, giving them the best equipment and the best training, and by paying constant attention to their health, we can be reasonably sure that the crews will be ready by the time the rocketships are.

We can imagine that, someday in the future, men will take space for granted and laugh at our worries now—they will be able to laugh, because our scientists did a good job of worrying about the best answers to all the problems of space.

CHAPTER 7

the wonderful spacesuit

EVERYONE who has read a science-fiction magazine, or even walked past a magazine stand, knows what spacesuits will look like—if you can trust the artists! How close to the truth are these illustrations?

Well, to begin with, it seems there will be two types of suits. One will look like a diver's suit, complete with heavy boots and mittens, a heavy plastic bowl on top and big tanks attached on the back. This outfit will be worn by men. For some reason that I do not quite understand, artists seem to think that women are much stronger, tougher and thicker-skinned than men; they also seem to think that women have no need to breathe.

So we have the second type of spacesuit. This one consists of some fancy kind of bathing suit worn by the girl, and a plastic bubble around her head that seems to fit tightly against her throat but will not even muss her hair when she puts it on. There are no mittens or boots. Usually there is not even a tank to supply the air she breathes!

Of course this picture is a piece of nonsense created by artists and editors to make the covers look prettier. Yet, among people who have given a lot of serious thought to how a spacesuit should be made, there is almost as much disagreement about the designs as there is difference in the two types artists draw. We can be sure that men and women will wear the same type of suit in space. (There certainly will be women in space! Scientists have already told us that women may be even better adapted to space than men!) Whether both men and women will wear such things as the diving suits, garments more like the bathing suits, or something different from either, is still being argued about.

Let us begin by finding out what a spacesuit must do. We can presume that spacesuits will be needed, since accidents will sometimes happen, and since men who begin building the space stations will have to work in space. We can start by deciding that spacesuits may be needed for several hours at a time, and that men must be able to move about in them and to perform work. Now what else?

The first purpose of a spacesuit is to provide air for the wearer to breathe. Oxygen must be supplied, and the carbon dioxide given off by the lungs must be removed. The latter can be done by running the air through one of several different chemicals which will remove carbon dioxide. Breathing through a tube into limewater will do this, as can be seen from the white, chalky precipitate which results, though there are other more convenient ways. The oxygen will have to come from a tank and be measured out by some kind of valve to keep it at the right pressure.

The way to supply the oxygen needs no further study. The United States Army has already solved this problem for high-altitude pilots who must have oxygen supplied to them. A man needs only about 3 pounds of pure oxygen in 24 hours, and that amount can be put in a much smaller tank—and a lighter one—than is usually pictured. He can carry a day's supply with no trouble, if he has a way of removing the carbon dioxide from the air he exhales, instead of wasting air into space. A fairly small device could be built to circulate air and pump it through chemicals, perhaps powered by the force of the oxygen released from the tank.

The second function of the spacesuit is to keep enough pressure around the body to make breathing possible and life comfortable. Here is where trouble begins to arise over our choice of suits.

The human body can stand a change of pressure downward, even a lowering by 15 pounds per square inch—as much as the change from normal air pressure to nothing —under some conditions. Divers can come up from 30 pounds pressure to 15, and if there has been no nitrogen in their air supply to cause bends, no real harm will be done. Men will not explode in space from the loss of pressure, even without suits. The human body naturally has as much pressure inside it as the air has outside, to balance; and it can soon adjust to new pressures. Even a sudden change of 15 pounds is not enough to defeat the remarkable strength that is built into that body.

However, reducing the outside pressure to zero brings problems that are not just those of a pressure difference. At zero pressure, oxygen in the lungs would rush out into space, and there would be no way to breathe. At the same time, the old expression about "blood boiling" would come true, with no need for anger. We know that the temperature at which water boils is lower when the pressure drops, as when the water is boiled high up on a mountain. When zero pressure is reached, water will boil at the temperature of the human body. The water in the blood would not be able to boil off through the skin—hence, no explosion—because of the amazing power of that skin to hold some pressure. In the lungs, on the other hand, the water would quite literally boil away. Hence, some pressure must be maintained in the lungs, and that means some pressure outside, to balance, so that breathing can go on without too much effort.

The suit must regulate the temperature within limits we can stand, and filter out the dangerous radiation from the Sun; the latter job is not too hard, since light can be cut off with a fairly thin filter. Holding the correct temperature is another matter. In sunlight, too much heat would strike the suit; in the shadow, there would be only a loss of heat.

Adding heat causes no trouble—it could be supplied by a battery and a few heating wires, since the body would lose heat quite slowly in a vacuum. Getting rid of too much heat is the big stumblingblock. The oxygen flowing from the tank would absorb some heat, since a gas soaks up heat as it expands. With the help of a highly reflective covering on the suit to keep the heat out, this might be enough. Rather than to try to cool the spacesuit, it would be better to design it to reflect all heat, and add heaters to provide any warmth needed.

The spacesuit would also require some means to remove the moisture from the air, since both the lungs and the body give off water. The same unit that removed the carbon dioxide could probably take care of the moisture with the aid of one of the chemicals that absorb water readily.

So far, it looks easy enough to design a suit. Such a suit will be much like the diver's suit, made of airtight fabric, blown up with air from a tank, and probably painted a brilliant white or silver. We will need thick, insulated soles on the boots and heavy insulation on the mittens to handle objects which may be too hot or too cold. And there we have it—or do we?

Well, a man could live in such a suit, but how well he could work in one is another matter. Unless we are quite clever with the design, we are going to be in trouble from the pressure inside.

To demonstrate this, take a balloon—one of the toy type—and blow it up. It should be one of the long ones, so that it can be bent after it is fully inflated. As you bend one end, you will notice that it seems fairly stiff and resists such bending, though the rubber used in it is limp and soft enough to bend from a breath. If you watch carefully, you may see why. As you bend it, parts of the balloon seem to be inflated more.

The reason is that bending changes the shape of a balloon enough to decrease the amount of space inside it. A bent pipe will always hold less than a straight one, provided the walls are held rigid enough to prevent stretching. You can also see this with a garden hose. With water pressure in it, it is much harder to bend.

When our hero in the spacesuit tries to bend his arm, he cannot do it without increasing the pressure inside! The suit is going to try to spread itself out in whatever position provides the most capacity, and then stay there.

It will not be so bad as some writers have thought. The man inside will be able to bend his limbs somewhat, since good design can keep the pressure change down, but without some means to ease that pressure, it is going to be hard for him to work. Besides, the constant changing of pressure as he moves would be highly uncomfortable.

This change of pressure has led some designers to plan a suit like a tank, or small rocketship. There would be no place for arms or legs. It would be propelled by a small rocket, with the man in the hollow shell. For arms it would have mechanical grapples, like those on a steam shovel, which would move outside the pressurized hull by means of electric motors!

Maybe this is the right kind of suit. Some expert engineers have proposed it, but others have disagreed. There is plenty of room for opinion and argument here, unfortunately. Possibly any one of several ways of building the suit would work. Certainly all styles will have been tested and the most suitable selected before the first spaceship takes off.

In my own opinion—and I am not an expert on spacesuits—the men who are proposing such completely mechanical suits are being too fearful of space. Such suits are going to weigh much more than they should, and in rocket work every pound counts. The suits will need a good deal of equipment to power the mechanical arms, and those arms will not be as good for all kinds of work as human arms and hands—even when those hands are in heavy mittens. There is also more mechanism to go wrong with such a device than with a simpler suit.

One of the answers is to lower the pressure inside the less-complicated suit. If pure oxygen is used at 3 pounds pressure (which will provide the same amount of oxygen to the lungs as our normal mixture of nitrogen and oxygen at 15 pounds), coping with the change of pressure becomes much easier. We can make the joints well enough so that no really great change in volume occurs with the bending of the limbs. Then the man in the suit will be able to do the work needed to perform a motion. A man's arm is more than strong enough to compress 2 cubic feet of air (or more) at 3 pounds per square inch pressure—enough to reduce its volume by half a cubic foot. There almost certainly will not be that much difference in volume; it would be a clumsy designer who permitted such changes in volume.

If we wanted to waste a little air—which we could afford to do for a few hours in the suit—it could be arranged by valves so that any increase in pressure blew a little air into space, and any decrease freed more from the tank. Even with that, the pressure change would be too small to matter, and no great amount of added weight or equipment would be needed.

Another advantage of the lower pressure obtained by using pure oxygen is that any tiny hole or tear in the suit would be less dangerous. There would be less tendency for the inside pressure to make the hole even bigger, and less shock to the body from the loss of pressure. For the few seconds needed to get a patch in place, the tank could probably supply enough oxygen to handle the loss.

We can also use somewhat lighter fabric —perhaps even fabric light enough and elastic enough to take up most of the pressure changes without the need of valves. We do not need heavy suits for temperature regulation. The vacuum outside is the best insulator there is, and a very thin layer of fabric covered with highly reflective paint will keep back the heat from the Sun almost as well as will a material of a much heavier construction.

It seems likely both the tanklike outfit and the diver's-suit type will be used. The one may prove better for some uses than the other, while the second may be best in still other cases.

There has even been some serious discussion given to suits more like those worn by the girls on the covers of magazines. We cannot really wear nothing but bathing suits in space, even with a bubble on our heads to supply oxygen to our lungs. (Pressure from the oxygen on the inside of the lungs must be balanced by pressure outside to make breathing possible for any length of time.) For a very short period, the bathing-suit affair might be enough—or even a normal suit of clothes, with an oxygen helmet. This type, though, would be used only as an emergency affair, and might prove very painful in even a few minutes, if not fatal.

Still, it appears that a suit could be designed which would not require that most of it be inflated at all.

The development of the simpler spacesuit almost certainly is not something that will be accomplished on the first trips into space. That type of suit might never work, but it is worth thinking about.

Suppose we keep the plastic helmet and air supply. Let the section around the lungs be the usual inflated tube, puffed out just a trifle beyond the skin, so that air pressure surrounds the lungs. We are still dealing with only 3 pounds pressure of oxygen. Now taper the inflated tube down at the shoulders and waist and change to an elastic fabric that will be skintight over legs, arms and hips. This fabric can be woven or formed so that it will have almost exactly 3 pounds pressure against the skin for every square inch. Yet when we move, there is no change of air pressure at the joints, because the fabric fits against our skin snugly.

We can still cover the material with reflective paint and weave tiny heating wires through it to take care of the temperature. We can even make it just a bit porous, so that perspiration can work through and evaporate into space—as it will do at once. Our bodies naturally cool themselves and maintain an even temperature by control-

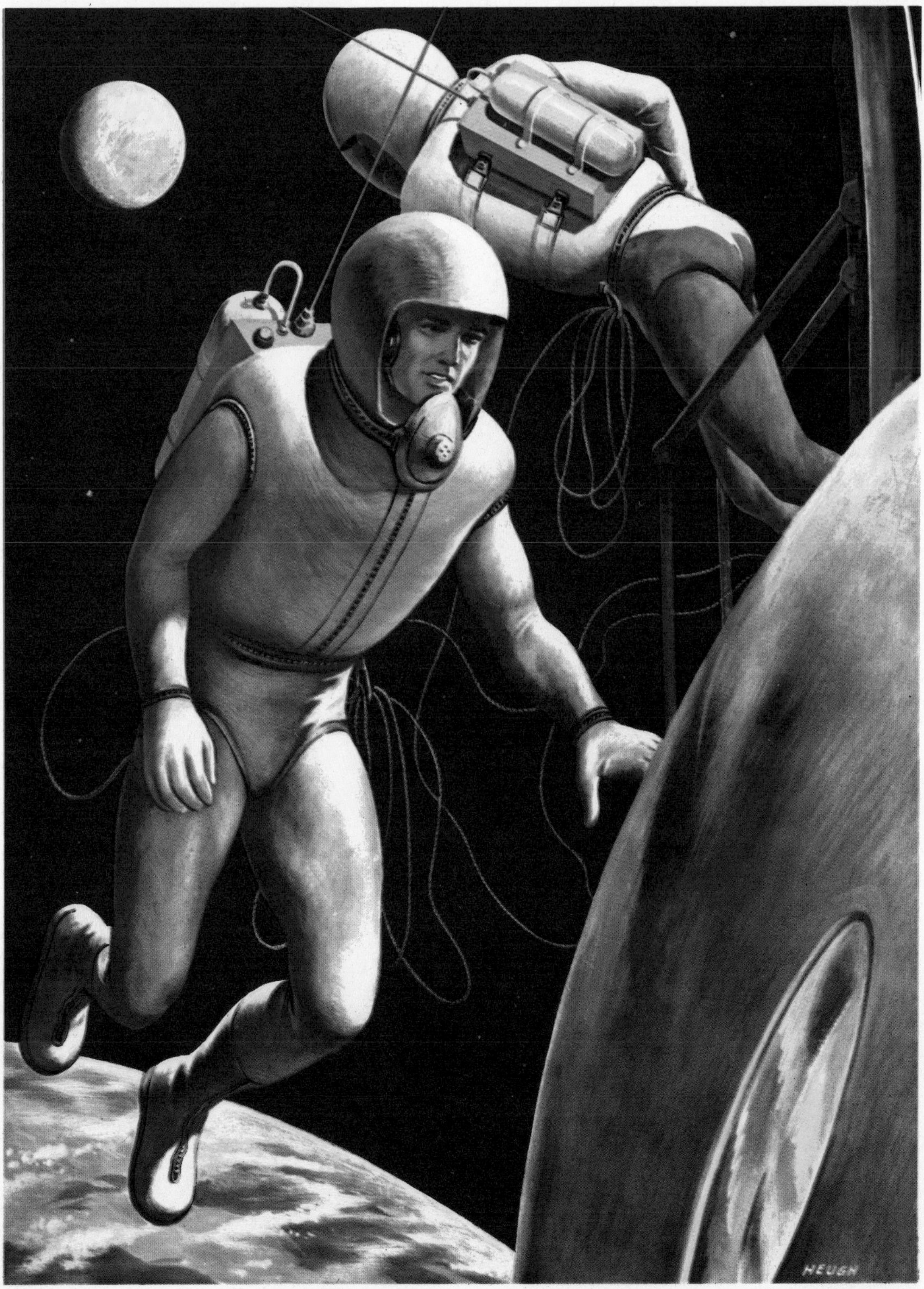
HEUGH

ling the amount of perspiration. The same thing might happen while wearing our spacesuit. If the body became too warm, we would perspire more, and so increase the cooling. Or if we grew too cold, the perspiration would lessen, reducing the cooling. By using some kind of porous underclothing, the perspiration from even the sections inside the pressurized and inflated part of the suit might reach the cooling sections. There would be some loss of oxygen this way, but it could be kept to a level that would not matter for short periods of time.

Perhaps even the part of the suit over the lungs could be devised of similar elastic material, so that there would be oxygen only in the helmet. In that case, instead of huge, bulky suits, we might have something that looked like the tights male ballet dancers wear.

Such simplified suits are not being planned now, as far as I know. Whether they will ever be used is a question. It seems certain, however, that, with time and experience, the wonderful and awkward covering now designed as a spacesuit can be simplified and made a lot more comfortable.

Despite all our speculation, the first suits will likely be similar to those in the familiar picture of a diver, however. There is no reason why the suits have to be the way they are, except that they are simply following a pattern already in use. We began with flyers' high-altitude suits, and we shall probably improve these, until we get our first spacesuit. Since the high-altitude suits look something like the diving suit, the spacesuit undoubtedly will, also.

After all, the automobile looked like a buggy long after there was no need for such a shape. It still has its engine in the front, where the horses used to be! By the same token, we are used to the familiar bulky, inflated suit already, and that is the type which probably will be adopted.

CHAPTER 8

free fall forever

LIKE most writers of science fiction 15 years ago, I tried to make the science in my stories accurate. When I wrote about space flight back in those days before real rockets were in operation, I worked out careful pages of mathematics covering every trip, and I tried to imagine everything in space correctly. I had already been thinking about space for more than 10 years, so I should have been reasonably accurate.

Yet in one story I erred in one of the most basic facts. A rocketman today would groan in horror when reading that story. Yet somehow, no reader caught the error and the editor never seemed to notice it. I did not spot it myself until the story was reprinted years later. I am still ashamed of my mistake, though I have since learned that many other writers—even fairly recent ones—have been making the same mistake.

I suppose that incident shows how hard it is to get used to thinking in terms of space. Things we take for granted on Earth simply are not the same in space.

Anyhow, I had the hero of the story cut off the rockets after his ship reached space 4,000 miles up. He then turned and walked back while the ship was drifting without power, and said something about the pull of gravity being only one-quarter what it was on Earth.

To make that statement was pure nonsense! Oh, the speaker was right about the figure for gravity at that distance, but in a ship with power turned off, he could not have walked, and he would not have felt any gravity. He would have been completely weightless, because there is no weight inside a ship when it is in *free fall*. That ship was in a state of free fall the moment the rockets stopped driving it ahead.

In fact, except when the rockets are being used to change the speed or direction of a ship in space, that ship is always in free fall. It does not matter whether it is moving off toward the Moon, circling around the Earth, or actually falling back.

To understand why, let us first get some of our facts about movement in space correct, and then look at the meaning of free fall carefully. To begin, we have to refer back to the same Sir Isaac Newton who explained that action and reaction had to be equal and in opposite directions. He worked out another law that applied to motion: Every object will continue forever at the same speed and in the same direction unless it is acted on by some force. Thus there would be no change in speed (which includes a speed of zero, or rest) or direction without some force being used to change it.

In space, this means that there would be

no change in speed or direction without either power from the rockets or a pull of gravity from some other body, usually. Speed by itself means nothing to those inside the ship, since they cannot feel it. (We do not feel the speed of the Earth around the Sun, for instance, though it is traveling at 18 miles a second.) What our bodies do feel and resist is a change in speed, which can be felt when the rockets work, just as we can feel resistance when a car is speeded up.

This change in speed is called acceleration, no matter in which direction it occurs. We sometimes refer to a reduction of speed as deceleration, but that is just another form of acceleration.

Now let us examine that state of free fall again. In the case of a ship falling back to Earth, with no air to slow it and no power working from its rockets, it is easy to see why the ship is said to be falling freely. Here gravity is acting on it, accelerating the ship's speed back toward Earth. Gravity, then, is the force acting to change its speed. There is no resistance, and the ship is responding exactly to the pull of the planet below it.

That is what free fall means—completely free or unresisting response to gravity.

If the ship is 4,000 miles up, gravity will add 8 feet per second of speed to it for every second gravity works on it as it falls back toward the surface. (On the surface, this pull of gravity is equal to 32 feet per second for each second it operates, and this amount of pull is called our standard *one gravity,* or 1 *g.*)

Suppose the ship is speeding away from Earth? Gravity will still operate to change the ship's speed by 8 feet a second for each second of pull. After 1 second, the ship will have lost 8 feet a second of speed; after 10 seconds, it will be going 80 feet a second slower, etc. That is just as much a fall as in the first case, because the word "fall" really means either a loss of speed away from Earth or a gain of speed toward Earth.

In the situation of a ship moving 7 miles a second as it reaches space from Earth, gravity will keep pulling it back; but its speed is so great that it will keep moving out into weaker and weaker gravity, where the loss of speed will become less and less. In this case, it will move more and more slowly, but its speed loss will never be quite so much as the weakening of gravity, and it will escape Earth, never to return. Seven miles a second is called the *speed* or *velocity of escape* from Earth.

As long as a ship is moving with no power —no matter where in space it may be—some gravity is operating on it, and it can truly be said to be in a state of free fall.

There can be no weight in such a ship in free fall, as I already said. The reason can be given in several different ways, but all really mean the same thing. We can say that weight is the resistance to gravity, which is a true definition. You cannot feel gravity, but you can feel any resistance to it, as when the floor stops you from falling. Even in diving off a high board, you cannot really feel weight until your fall is stopped, though this is for such a short time that you seldom notice it.

In the ship in free fall, there is no resistance. The ship is being pulled back with exactly the same change of speed as your body, so there is nothing to offer any resistance.

Another way to put it is to say that your body, so there is nothing to offer any —just as it resists slowing down when the brakes are jammed on suddenly in a car. *Inertia,* or the resistance to such a change, is pulling you forward. Gravity, on the other hand, is pulling you back. Here, they exactly balance each other, so the feeling of pull in either direction is canceled out, and there is no weight.

Wheeoo!

It took me over 10 years to learn all that completely, so I will not be surprised if others find it hard to accept the explanation immediately. These facts about rockets are probably the most difficult to understand, since they are not very normal to the world about us on which we have to base our thinking. Yet, when we really look about us, it is not so different, after all. The idea of something falling while going up seems strange, but a stone thrown straight up does begin to fall the second it leaves your hand—otherwise it would keep on rising. The idea of something going on at the same speed forever without some force to slow it down will not work on Earth. That is only because air resistance and friction are always exerting such a slowing force.

Even the lack of weight is not entirely strange. Most of us have felt ourselves growing lighter in an elevator when it starts a rapid descent, or as we speed downward on a steep roller coaster.

Perhaps the hardest idea to accept is the statement that objects keep going in the same direction unless acted on by some force. We see cars turn in a circle, even with their motors off; planes swing around even when gliding; and a hundred other cases can be brought to mind. Yet the resistance to change in direction can be felt. Every time we turn a corner at high speed, our bodies lean in the direction we were going before. The reason we can turn is that there is something acting to turn us. In the plane, we use air resistance; on the ground, we use the fact that it is easier for the wheels to roll than to slide sidewise. A sled will not often turn on smooth ice, because there is not enough friction to overcome the tendency to go straight.

In space, nothing can turn a ship off to the side except gravity or a side thrust from rockets. (We can turn the ship over or move it around on its axis by means of *gyroscopes.* When we turn the gyroscope in one direction, we get an opposite reaction from the ship by having it make part of a turn in the other direction. Thus a thousand turns of a one-pound gyroscope would turn a thousand-pound ship once in the opposite direction. This motion would not change its direction, but only its position, or the way it pointed along its course.)

The comic strips do show rockets turning around in nice little circles, just like airplanes, but such turns will not really work. To move backward from its original direction, a rocket would have to blast out hard enough to cancel all its forward motion, and then build up a new speed in the other direction. To do that would waste altogether too much fuel. A little side motion can be added to the forward motion for correcting an orbit. Mostly, though, ships are going to be aimed at their destination before they take off, and then they are going to follow that course as directly as they can. Any curving in the path will be caused by gravity from the Sun or some planet.

The only instance where a ship can move in a circle is around a planet, and in that case the gravity of the planet acts on the ship, much as a string will hold a weight to a circular path, when the weight is twirled. This, of course, gives us the circular orbit around the Earth which will be followed by the satellites we first send up—or by our first true space station.

The Moon describes a similar orbit around the Earth, just as the Earth circles around the Sun, and is kept from going off on a straight line into space by the gravity of the Sun.

One of the questions asked about such an orbit is: Why won't the ship fall back to Earth?

Unless the speed of the ship is high

enough, it will! Or at least the ship will fall back toward the Earth until the fall gives it enough speed to go into a new circular orbit, where speed and gravity are in balance. Once this balance is reached (and provided there is height enough left to avoid air resistance), the ship can go on circling the Earth forever in such an orbit, just as the Moon goes on circling in its orbit.

The answer to the question lies in the same law of Newton already given. The resistance to change in direction, or inertia, tends to make the ship move in a straight line, which would carry it farther and farther from Earth. If you draw a circle for Earth and a bigger one around the first for the orbit, then lay a ruler along the orbit and draw a straight line along the edge, you will see that the line gets farther from Earth as it heads out away from the circles.

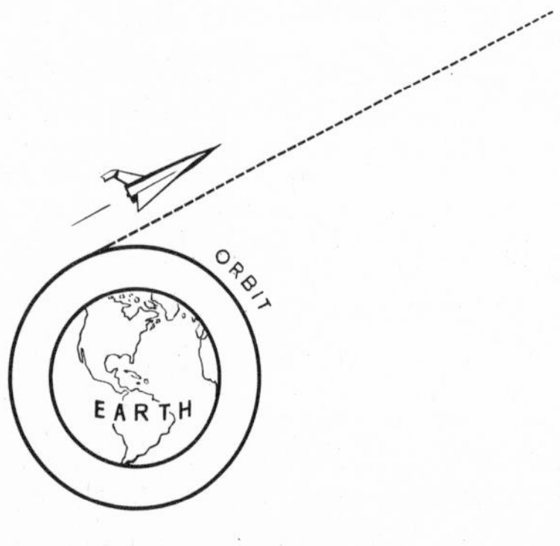

The gravity of the planet tends to make the ship fall back toward the Earth, of course. Hence, to get a circular orbit, all one has to do is to give the ship the right horizontal speed. Then the downward pull of gravity and the outward force of inertia will exactly balance, and the ship will stay at the same distance from the planet, forming a circular orbit.

The forward speed will remain the same around the orbit. Neither gravity nor inertia is working sideways to slow the ship, and there is no resistance from air or friction. Thus, it takes no work at all to keep the ship going at the same rate.

This is another and highly special form of free fall. The ship does not seem to change speed either toward or away from Earth; nevertheless, it is falling all the time.

Just remember that the normal path of the ship would be the straight line you drew. Now, obviously, to stay in the circle, it has to fall below the line! If the Earth were a flat plain stretching out far enough, the ship would fall toward it, but as fast as the ship falls, the Earth bends around under it. At each point on the orbit of the ship, there would be a new straight line that could be drawn, and the ship would still be falling away from that line toward Earth.

A shell fired from a gun forms a wide curve as it falls toward Earth. If it fires for a long distance, the curvature of the Earth will actually make it travel farther before it touches the surface—considerably farther than if the Earth were flat. The longer the distance the shell goes, the greater distance it has to fall to Earth. If the shell could be fired far enough, it might also reach a level where it could not fall back, because the Earth would be curving away as fast as the shell could fall. It would still be a true fall, even though the shell would then be in just such an orbit as our ship.

A ship set up into such an orbit can be in free fall forever. Inside the ship, men will still be weightless for the same reasons. Inertia and gravity are still in balance, neutralizing each other. We can call the inertia here centrifugal force, as we did earlier in the book. The name will not matter, since both inertia and centrifugal force are exactly the same thing in the case of anything whirling in a circle. (Centrifugal force is only the resistance to change in direction. Anyone who tries whirling the weight at the end of a string we have used as an example will soon realize that this can be a powerful force. If you release the string, the weight will fly off rapidly in a straight line, just as the ship would without gravity.)

This idea of a balance of inward pull by gravity and outward force because of inertia or centrifugal force was more of a problem than the wisest men could work out for thousands of years. They saw the planets moving around the Sun—they even guessed that they were worlds like our own—but they could not understand how they moved. Even after the invention of the telescope, the problem remained unsolved until Newton finally found the answer, less than 300 years ago. Then, after he had proposed his solution, some very learned men were still unable to understand it.

We have grown used to the law since his time, and every scientist today accepts it.

It is fortunate for us that things do work this way, too. It means that we can not only get into space in our ships, but that we can stay there after we have built a station, without having to burn more rocket fuel to keep it going!

SECTION III

to the moon

CHAPTER 9

station in space

As we have seen, men can get into space and reach a permanent orbit around Earth with a three-stage rocketship, but while the ship could keep on circling year after year, the men could not very well continue to live in it. Neither could the ship carry enough equipment necessary to do the things we want to do.

Something larger and more complete is needed for our first real outpost in space. We need a base where a crew of some size can live with some comfort, and where we can carry on scientific work month after month. That means plenty of room for them—and such room will mean more material than a single rocketship could lift.

When we begin designing an outpost in space, we soon find that it will be much too enormous to shoot up from the surface. There would also be a great deal of waste in trying to send such a base up from Earth, since it would have to be built strongly enough to stand the high acceleration of the trip, though no great strength would be needed after it was up.

Such a station must be built in space. There have been several stories written about building it on Earth and transporting it into space, but that is as impractical as moving a flock of cows, chickens and other animals into an apartment instead of keeping them on the farm and moving only the eggs, milk and meat. It simply does not make good sense to try it.

There have been quite a few suggestions for such a station, since the idea is almost as old as the idea of the rocketship. Even the height at which it will be put in its orbit has been set at distances as close as 300 miles and as far out as 22,000 miles. The station we probably will build will be very much like the one designed by Dr. von Braun.

The station will be put up at a height where it will rotate around the Earth once every 2 hours—that is, a height of 1,075 miles above the surface. This distance is far enough to be clear of the last thin wisps of air, yet not too far to be reached easily by the ships, nor too far for clear observation of the Earth below.

The station could be put at some other height near that figure, but then its orbit around the Earth would take an odd number of hours, minutes and seconds. We do not have to work out the orbit to exact hours, but things will be much simpler in many ways if we can be sure—both on the station and below—of where the station will be at any time, without having to consult fancy tables and charts. After all, wouldn't it be nice to have the Moon make its circle in exactly 28 days, so that we could predict it easily? Or to have Earth move around the Sun in just 360 days, to give us 12 exact months of 30 days with no leap years? We cannot do anything about the laws on which our calendar system is based, but we can give the station a handy orbit.

The station will have to be large enough for about 80 or more men to stay on it for months at a time, which means a rather big station. Since men cannot work too well at many things without their having some feeling of weight, we will have to provide for that angle. The easiest way is to make the station circular and spin it about its hub. Then there will be centrifugal force at the rim of the station, just as there is in a circular orbit, or in our familiar weight being whirled at the end of a string. If we build the station with a diameter of about 200 feet and spin it around once each 22 seconds, we shall have an outward pressure at the rim of about one-third normal gravity. This will grow less as we move inward toward the hub, since the size of the circle is smaller near the center.

This project begins to look like a really large one. However, the station will not be all solid from rim to hub. The rim will actually be a big tube, looking something like a doughnut. From the rim, we can run a couple of hollow shafts back to the hub. The hub will be fixed so it can serve as the entry port. It would be hard to load and unload into a port on the spinning rim, but at the hub there will be less motion, and we can even eliminate most of that. The hub can be turned by a motor enough to make it stop rotating when we want it to.

We shall need power to run all the machinery on the station, too, but for this we can use the light from the Sun. If we put a trough on top of the station and set it to reflect light onto a pipe, we can heat mercury by sunlight, and that element can operate a turbine engine, just as steam would. We do not need any heavy, possibly dangerous, atomic motor, and, in addition, our power is now free and will run as long as we want it.

Now if we include all the air supplies, the food and water, the machines, living quarters, telescope, radar equipment and other things, we have a station that weighs thousands of tons. The construction will be a tremendous undertaking, but not an impossible one. Dr. von Braun has designed the station so that no piece of equipment is either too heavy or too bulky to be taken up by one of the three-stage rockets.

The biggest problem will be to find the money needed. A station such as that will cost about 4 billion dollars—twice as much as the amount needed for the development of the atom bomb. However, huge as that figure is, it is not very big when compared to the total expenditures of the Government in a year. Also, the cost can be spread over several years.

Let us suppose the money has been provided by the Government, and that the rocketships have all been built, along with the parts for the station. (The sum of money required for building the station, incidentally, will also include all the funds needed to build enough supply rockets.) Now how do we get all the parts together in space?

Well, there will have been previous flights up to the orbit to test everything and to survey what must be done. Now the big three-stage rocket will be waiting, loaded with parts, and with the first few construction engineers aboard. At the proper time, the huge first stage will blast out, and the rocket will rise on a pillar of fire, almost straight up for the first few miles, before it begins to turn on its synergy curve. The first stage will burn out and begin to drop back to the ocean below, where ships will recover it for use again. The second stage will fire until it uses all its fuel, and then it will also drop to the ocean for recovery. Nothing will be wasted in this operation.

For a few seconds longer, the small, plane-like first stage will be blasting. Then it will cut off and rise outward, coasting on its speed. The pull of the Earth will slow it, since it is in free fall, but its speed will carry it up to the 1,075-mile height. There, for a few seconds, the rocket will blast again, correcting the orbit to a true circle around the Earth. When the rocket cuts off, the men will begin unloading quickly, shoving the material out into space. These men will be dressed in spacesuits now, working in the airless cargo compartment.

As the material is shoved out, it simply floats along beside the rocket, since it has the same speed and path in space, and is kept in its orbit exactly as is the ship. The men will be weightless, but they will be able to move about by using tiny rockets that they can hold in their hands. It will not take much power to give them the motions they need. It will take much skill, but the men will have had practice on the earlier trial flights.

Once everything is unloaded in space, the ship will blast backward to cut its speed and begin falling back to Earth. It will land by cutting into the atmosphere and slowing against the air, using its wings for support now as it is coasting downward.

The men left behind will now begin working quickly. Their first job is to provide for themselves a place to live. To do this, they must put together one section of the big tube that will form the rim of the station. Using the hand rockets, they will hook onto sections of the tube and begin pulling these together. Everything will be coded so there can be no mistake, and these few men will have practiced the assembly dozens of times on Earth.

The cylinder begins to take shape now—big, 30 feet in diameter, and even longer than that.

As the men work, another rocket will come up from Earth and other men will begin unloading more sections. These are now put together by both first and second crews. An air lock is installed, and the ends of the cylinder are sealed with bulkheads. Now the men have living quarters. The big tanks of air which the ships are bringing up are coupled to valves, and oxygen begins feeding into the cylinder. Tanks of water, cases of food, and equipment for living are rapidly moved into the quarters—or these may have been moved in first, while the walls were still going up.

Now for the first time, it will be possible for the men to move inside their quarters and take off their spacesuits to rest and sleep. With this section built, other men can also come up to increase the crew. The really critical part of the job is over.

There still will be no weight. Power will have to be supplied by batteries, and used carefully until the crew can get far enough along to install the final power plant—but they can live, even though it will not be comfortable living. They will have one comfort, however, that cannot be had on Earth—their beds will be the softest in the whole Solar System, because they can sleep right in the air, using only a couple of cords or a light sack to keep them from drifting off.

From this point on, the work will be hard but not too difficult. Supplies will come up on regular schedules. Soon a tiny rocketship—like a small blimp, with a rocket motor behind—will be brought up, to be used as a taxi between ship and station, and as a tractor for moving supplies around. The rim of the station will keep growing from each end until it can be joined into a full circle. The spokes will run inward and join

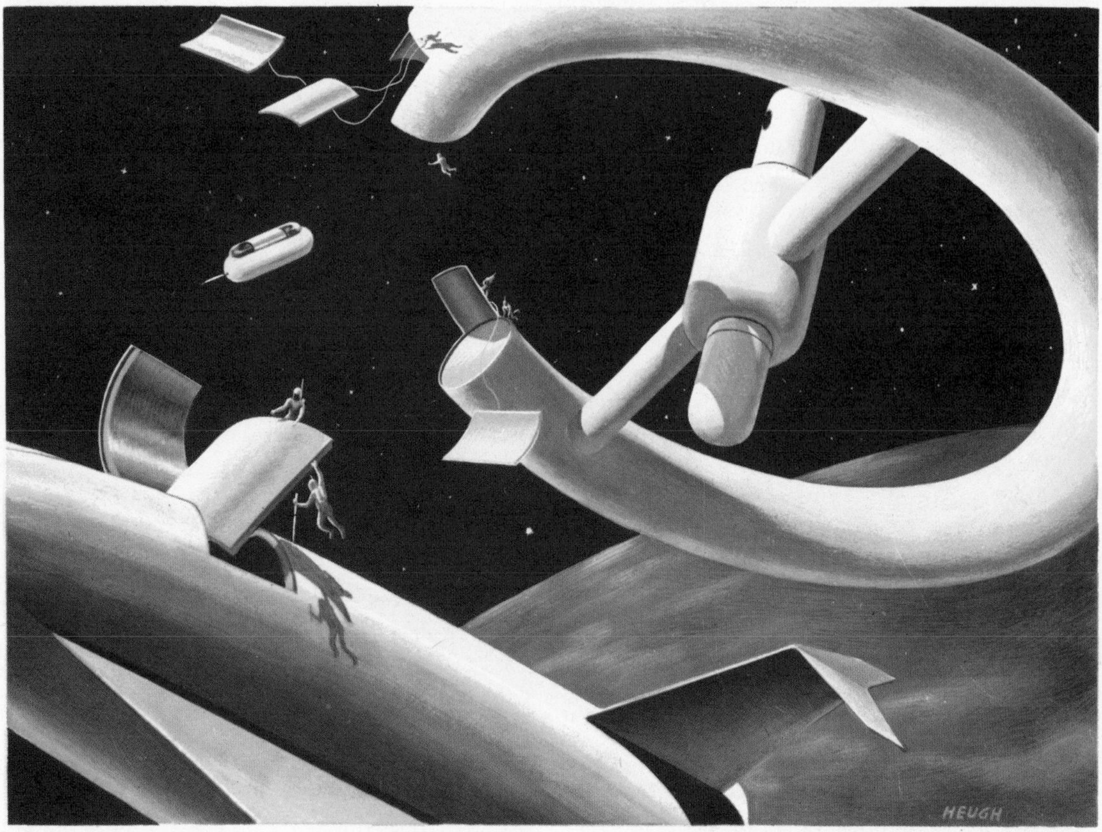

the hub. The heavier machinery will then be installed, while experts begin putting together the power equipment, radar antennae, and all the complicated maze of wires, pipes, tubes and countless other materials.

Once the main details are finished, small rocket motors will be attached to the rim of the station to spin it, while other motors will be mounted to keep the top turned to the Sun. Only a little power will be needed, since this correction in position needs only enough energy to turn the ship over once a year—a few degrees at a time at perhaps weekly intervals.

Now, with weight to keep things in place and add to the comfort, the "garden" is installed. It will consist of tanks of plants that will grow under sunlamps. These plants will give the station an almost permanent air supply.

Men breathe in oxygen, and their lungs give off water and carbon-dioxide gas (the products of burning sugar and starch in the body with the oxygen they breathe in). Plants grow by taking energy from sunlight and using it by means of the green *chlorophyll* in their leaves to reverse the process—they use water and the carbon in carbon dioxide to create sugar and starch, and give off free oxygen.

Thus, by keeping a balance between the human and plant population of the station, the same air can be used almost indefinitely. All water given off (except that used by the plants) can also be collected and distilled for reuse. This makes the station largely self-sustaining and greatly lightens the loads of supplies needed from Earth.

The plants will not take up much space, either, since a great many of them can be put into tanks that will require only a small room to house them. Most of the plants will be selected for their speed of oxygen release, but probably some food plants will be raised, to give the men fresh vegetables now and then.

In theory, this world could be like a separate one, completely self-sufficient. Nothing would be lost, and, given power from the Sun, everything used could be recovered for use again. Actually, the men will not try to make it work that well, but the quantity of supplies needed from Earth will be less than you might think.

Finally, there will come the scientists and their equipment. They will begin studying the Earth below, seeing what makes the weather behave as it does for one thing. With such a good opportunity to study everything on Earth, scientists will know exactly where storms are brewing. They will be able, after some study, to predict the weather accurately weeks in advance. These forecasts will more than repay the cost of the station. In even one year, the savings from loss due to bad weather can add billions of dollars to the value of the crops grown on Earth. Through this work alone, the station will prove to be one of the best investments ever made.

Much more work will be done. Here, with no air to make shaky, fuzzy images of the stars, astronomers will be able to set up a telescope that will give them information they have wanted to know for years. They will learn far faster now, and will also be able to study the Moon, Mars and the other planets in real detail.

Other men will have the wonderful opportunity to do research in a true vacuum. These men can let the air out of a whole section of the station and run the temperature as low as they wish. Chemical processes that have always been difficult to perform on Earth will frequently work easily in the true vacuum of space. New hormone and drug research can be tried.

Doctors will have a chance to study life without gravity, as will biologists. Both may learn a great deal more about how the cells —the basic building blocks of life—grow, and why things go wrong with them.

We cannot even begin to imagine how valuable the station will prove to be.

We shall have other advantages, too. The work done in improving the rockets and the search for better, lighter materials for the station will add to our advancement in a great many fields. Jet planes, automobiles, perhaps even furniture, will be improved as a result of research and study at the station.

Politically, military men in the station will be able to keep an eye on the whole world. Wars will be harder to start when armies can be seen grouping together. The stock of missiles on the station which can reach any spot on Earth will serve to make nations think twice before attacking each other. We hope it will help to put an end to aggressive war. Certainly almost nothing can be secret from the station. As it sweeps around the poles once every two hours, while the Earth revolves below it, it will cover every section of the world daily.

There will be another advantage, too. The station will provide a perfect place to build ships for the Moon and other planets, and will also serve as the takeoff point for journeys to those places. Most of the work involved in such interplanetary trips will have been done in getting things up to the station and giving them the speed needed to stay in such an orbit. From the station, the other worlds are actually easier to reach than it is to reach the station from Earth.

CHAPTER 10

life in the station

LET us move ahead a few years after the station is built and see what life out in space is going to be like. We shall select young Tom Augen to follow, since he is the son of one of the headmen, and will not have too much work to do, but will be free to move through most of the station. He has been down on Earth, finishing his studies, and is now on his way back to the station for his vacation.

Below, most of the Earth he can see from the rocket is dark, since it is night on that side. Still, there is enough light on some parts to show the huge globe below him, filling a large part of the heavens. Nothing on Earth can equal the impressive sight of the big globe as seen from the vicinity of the station.

Then the rocket corrects its course and comes to rest. Just ahead is the gleaming station, shining whitely in the light of the Sun on its top, except where a few panels have been turned to display their black side and absorb heat. Tom can barely see the underside of the big doughnut, however, by the dim light from Earth. No sunlight can reach the underside, since it is in the shadow of the top section. Without the reflection from Earth, it would be completely black.

The pilot points outside, and Tom stares through the viewing port, being very careful as he moves. After months spent on Earth, he has to be cautious in moving about without weight. Then he spies something heading for the rocket that looks like a sausage 20 feet long, and he knows that the taxi has come to pick him up.

Below, freight is being moved in the cargo hold of the rocket, but Tom pays little attention to the crates of carefully dehydrated food and the boxes of scientific equipment. He hears a clank as the taxi touches the rubbery seal of the lock, and then he sees the inner door being opened.

He needs no spacesuit, since the nose of the taxi just fits the opening in the rocket. Inside the little ship, his father is standing, and they greet each other and begin telling what each has been doing, while other men pack some of the cargo into the taxi. The pilot of the taxi soon closes the front section of the little ship, and it is kicked away from the larger ship.

Using small hand-powered gyroscopes, the pilot cranks busily, and the taxi begins turning end over end slowly. Finally, there is a short blast, and the taxi drifts back toward the station. Tom sees that the hub is being slowed to receive them. The basket-like frame in front of the hub normally

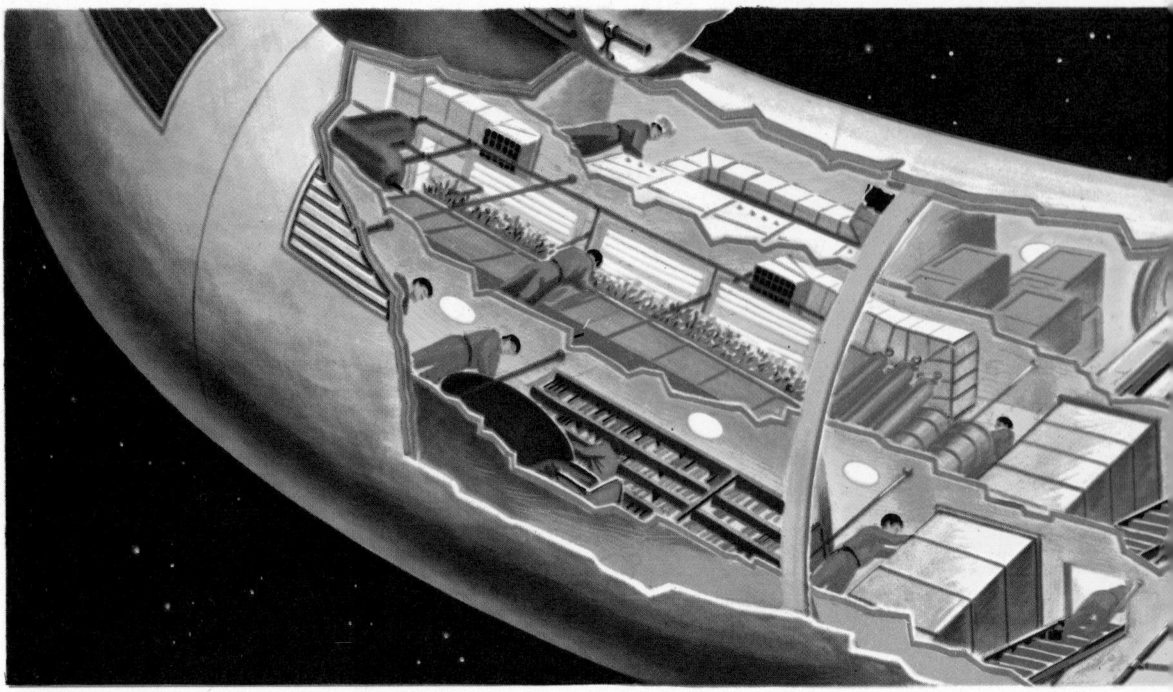

turns with the station, three times a minute. Now motors are slowing it, bringing the hub to rest. Soon the basket points steadily toward the taxi, and the little ship drifts into it. The taxi's slight speed is halted, and its nose sets against another airtight seal.

In the commissary where everyone eats, the cook makes a light snack for Tom. He eats it politely; it is not bad, but most of the food here has not so good a flavor as that on Earth, since it has to be processed to save weight, and to avoid too much waste.

Then Tom goes to his room, greeting old friends as he meets them. With less than 100 men here, everyone knows everyone else. Most of the men work up in the station on 3-month or 6-month shifts, with the same period back on Earth. A few, however, are doing work that cannot be interrupted. One man has been here since the station was completed.

In coming down from the hub after he arrived, Tom's weight had risen from nothing to just over 50 pounds—1/3 what he weighed on Earth—by the time he had reached the commissary located at the outer edge of the station. Now, as he heads for his sleeping quarters at the inner side of the hollow tube around the station, he grows several pounds lighter.

He has been looking forward to that. After sleeping with such low weight here at the station, even the best mattresses on Earth have seemed hard. He goes into the tiny cabin that is his home on board. It is as snug as it can be, with no wasted space, but there is room enough for him. There is the old, familiar feel of the steady current of air being blown from ducts in the walls.

That air current is the most vital thing on board. If a meteorite ever punctured the hull of this section, there would be no way to prevent the vital oxygen from rushing out into space, until the section could be patched. Automatic bulkheads would cut off this section of the station then, to protect other sections. Even though the punctured section could be cut off, the idea of a leak in the hull is always unpleasant.

Tom does not worry too much, though.

The inner section of the hull is made of fabric that holds the air, and beyond that is a *meteor bumper* of metal, designed to absorb the impact of any normal-sized meteorite. So far, no damage has been done that caused any trouble, and nobody really expects any great danger.

The noise in the station has been muffled by careful sound insulation, and Tom quickly falls asleep. In the morning, when he wakes, he feels more rested than he has for months. Living is a lot easier here in the lighter weight of the station.

As he goes to the bathroom to bathe and brush his teeth, he hears the "night" shift going off work. The station still runs on a 24-hour day, with 3 shifts of 8 hours each, though there is no true day or night here. Tom begins washing his face, wondering what they used for a washbowl before the station had spin to give it weight. He has heard about some of the trouble the early pioneers in space had keeping clean, but he has never seen how it was done.

On his way to breakfast, he asks his father how the first people in space managed. The older man grins. "They didn't keep very clean," he says. "They squirted a drop of water from a bottle onto a sponge and wiped off the worst dirt with that. The men were too busy getting the station built to worry about little things, though I guess they could have rigged up something better, using a stream of air to blow the water back down a drain."

Tom's father stops as a yell comes from the small galley where the food is prepared in electronic ranges. Tom can guess what is happening. The cook is training a new helper, who has not gotten used to the low weight here. In space, grease in a skillet will leap much farther than it would on Earth.

Then Tom's father goes off to his job of finishing a survey. Men are thinking again about running water from the Mediterranean Ocean into the Sahara Desert, where it would form a lake that would change the whole climate. Now that a bombing and survey section on the station has been established, the threat of war has been greatly decreased, and some of the money that formerly went for military expense is now being used to make the whole Earth more habitable by means of such big projects. Tom's father has to use the telescope here to study the whole territory of North Africa and find the best route for the new idea.

Much similar work is being done on the station. The scientists have even located new deposits of minerals on Earth, since some details show up much better from a distance.

Tom passes by the spoke to the hub, where a load of garbage and refuse is being put onto the elevator to be taken up and shipped back to Earth. That is one of the biggest problems. The crew cannot just eject refuse out into space, since it would follow in the same orbit and make trouble as it piled up. They cannot shoot it back to Earth, because it is not economical to waste rocket motors that way. So the men have to dehydrate all such refuse and press it into blocks; then the supply ships carry it back for disposal.

As the day passes, Tom wanders about from section to section. He visits the hydroponic tanks in the greenhouse, as the room is called. He is surprised to see some changes. Once, most of the plants were tanks of algae, able to release a great deal of oxygen rapidly. The section now has been rebuilt, and most of it seems to be filled with fast-growing lettuce, tomatoes and other plants. Tom learns that the algae are still there, but better handling methods have reduced the space needed, and the unused space has been filled with food plants. The men grow all the salad material they need now; after so much of the dehydrated food, they need some fresh greens.

Nearby, the pumps that handle the water are busy. With the arrival of new cargo and the packing of return goods in the hub, the weight on different sides of the station is being changed, and water has to be pumped around to equalize this weight; otherwise, the station would wobble instead of spinning smoothly. Here, in the "water" room, other machines are condensing moisture out of the air and storing it in tanks.

As Tom watches, a red light appears, and there is the sound of hissing. A pipe leading into the wall begins to collect a layer of frost.

Tom knows that the workers are pumping some of the excess water out into space. There is always an excess, since none is wasted on the station, and since even the most carefully dried food from Earth has some moisture that keeps adding to the supply. When there is too much moisture, some is let out into space, where it evaporates. The astronomers make a joke about it ruining the visibility, but it actually spreads out too quickly in the vacuum to have that effect.

The boy next visits the vast communications sections where men are in constant touch with Earth. At radar frequencies, it is easy to send any signal to Earth and back. Even a 100-watt transmitter would do a good job. All the ultra-high-frequency television broadcasts are received perfectly up here, as long as these are over the part of the world where the station is located. Posted in the recreation room, Tom finds a list of programs that can be seen from different countries at various times.

The weather-study room is next, but Tom does not stop there. Weather has become a very real science now, and the men talk in words that nobody could have understood a few years ago. They are now arguing whether there is going to be frost as far south as Pasadena forty days hence; they are preparing the fall weather report already. Someone is arguing that the cold weather could be delayed for several weeks more by using a new method of causing rainfall over the ocean in one place. They not only predict the weather, but sometimes they can even change it.

In another section of the station, the Earth below is projected on a big screen, and here Tom's father looks up and nods. Men in uniform are also studying the image. They keep a constant check. The telescope is in a tiny, separate structure, following the station's orbit, to permit the telescope to be mounted and moved more smoothly, without the spin of the station. Its signals are carried into the room by television.

At one time this was the only telescope in use; but since both the ground observers and the astronomers needed it full-time, another was constructed for astronomy.

Tom gets a glimpse of the astronomy room, but does not go in. The astronomers are even harder to understand than the weathermen. They have found something new, and now they are working to prove or disprove for once and for all whether the Universe is expanding. For some reason Tom cannot understand, the astronomers think this discovery will also provide a clue to understanding the nucleus of the atom.

Then Tom arrives at the laboratories. Here red lights are on over some of the doors, indicating that the rooms in which the researchers are working are in a completely vacuum condition. The air has been removed completely, and the men are busy with new experiments. Tom glances in through one quartz window, to see the wall covered with glowing little wires. These are the vacuum tubes—they need no glass bulb around them here, since they are automatically in a vacuum.

Tom wants to be a physicist himself, and to do research on some of the new ideas for rocket fuels that may someday be developed to work by atomic power, but he does not know enough yet to follow much of the work here.

The one experiment that interests him most is finished. A biologist had set up a laboratory in the hub for months and had begun growing giant amoebas. The single microscopic cells of the original creatures were kept free from weight and eventually some of them grew to be bigger than baseballs. The scientist claimed it gave him a much better view of what went on in living matter, and Tom had been greatly interested. But now the man was back on Earth, putting his results to work in one of the biggest hospitals.

Lunch has come and gone by this time, and the day is growing late. Tom glances at his watch and then heads toward the gymnasium. Up here, under the weakening effect of less weight and less need for hard work, muscles tend to grow soft. That would not matter if a man were to stay here the rest of his life, perhaps, but for him to return to Earth safely, his body must be kept in first-class condition. In fact, the body should be in better-than-average health in all ways, if it is to take the strain of the acceleration in the ships.

Once a week, men go out into space in their spacesuits to play various games, where the absence of weight makes skill in moving by means of rocket guns the most necessary qualification. This gives the men a good workout, since strenuous activity will strengthen the body, even without weight. Most of the time, however, they train in the gymnasium.

A fair number of men are there, working under a physical adviser. Tom moves about from horizontal bars to dumbbells, then puts on a group of weights that attach all over his body, and begins a complete workout. When he is finished, he is perspiring, but he knows he will not lose strength before returning to Earth in three months.

It is after dinner when the greatest thrill comes. Tom gets permission to borrow the taxi, and he travels back along the orbit to a place that lies 15 miles away. He has heard plenty about what is being done there, though the work was not started before he left space the last time. He has never had a chance to see it yet.

Then the project takes shape ahead of him. It is not much to look at—just a big dump of parts and a kind of tank that is being tested—but Tom does not care. He knows it is the start of the long-expected first trip to the Moon. By now, the station is familiar and not too exciting, but this is like a breath from the future.

Somehow, he is going on that trip to the Moon, if he can! Even if he has to miss the first journey, though, he is going sometime. Imagine—actually getting away from the Earth and the station to a brand-new world! That should be something to live for!

CHAPTER 11

step two—the moon

FOR YEARS after most of us knew that men would reach the Moon someday, many people were still thinking of making it in one jump. The idea was to take off from Earth and build up enough speed to go all the way to the big satellite. Because of this theory, most talk of rockets got mixed up with the idea of escape velocity.

Many people also still wonder about escape velocity. Actually, it has very little to do with space travel as we know it today. The seven-miles-a-second speed which is the velocity of escape from Earth can be forgotten. It would apply only if the rocket had to build up its speed in one great burst and then go on after that for some vast distance without using more fuel. Or it would apply to something shot away from Earth, like a cannon shell. In real space travel, it is not needed.

By building the space station first, we can simplify the whole operation of getting to the Moon. In fact, without first establishing an *orbital station,* it would be almost impossible to get to the Moon and still have enough fuel for the return. With such a station, the trip to our satellite becomes fairly easy.

To reach the station, a rocketship must build up a speed of about 18,000 miles an hour—that is, about 5 miles a second. This is the speed just as the blast is cut. (The German word *Brennschluss* is often used for the blast cutoff, and it simply means "end of burning.") Some speed is lost as the rocket rises against the pull of gravity, but at the station, the *orbital speed*—speed around Earth—is still more than 15,000 miles an hour.

A ship taking off from that orbit with such a speed is obviously starting off with over half the work done, even if it did need to reach escape velocity. Besides, though only a thousand miles has been covered, gravity has already dropped to about two-thirds of what it is on the surface of Earth, and the escape velocity from such an orbit would be lower. The first thousand miles represent far more than half of the effort needed to get to the Moon!

When we figure everything out carefully, it is surprising how little extra speed we need. If we can make our ship go 1 mile a second faster than the speed of the station, we can reach the Moon! Even a wartime V-2 rocket was able to accelerate to that speed—a mere 3,600 miles an hour. Hence, without any changes in its design, we could fire a V-2 from the station to the Moon, if we wished.

That would not allow us any fuel for the return to the station, however, and when men go to the Moon, they will want to get back. Getting back from the Moon is more of a problem. However, the gravity at the surface of the Moon is only about one-sixth that of Earth, and it falls off more quickly, too. The speed needed to leave the Moon will not cause too much trouble.

We could probably fuel the final stage of one of our rockets and send a man to the Moon in it. He would have to carry all possible fuel with him to make a landing, since there is no air on the barren surface of the Moon, and he can only set down safely by using his rockets as a brake to check his speed, but it might be done. Then if we could fire other unmanned ships to him with extra fuel, he might be able to make the return trip.

He could not do much exploring that way, however, and if we are going out to the Moon, we might as well get our money's worth. Also, engineers and scientists prefer to do things in the safest and best way, instead of indulging in stunts. So they have worked out the details of a complete expedition, designed to carry 50 men to the Moon, stay there for 6 weeks, and then return to the station.

Again, the plan has been worked out in its main details by Wernher von Braun, and it is one which requires no equipment other than that which we already have, or which we could build now if we had to. Probably there will be many improvements needed before the real trip to make it easier and simpler, but we could make it right now.

The first trip will be for exploration to locate a place to land. For that survey, we will build something like one of the small taxi rockets, but much larger and with extra fuel tanks. It will not be designed to land on the Moon, but only to circle around the satellite and head back, using lunar gravity to turn. It will not have to carry passengers (though this may be decided otherwise at the time), but it will take careful pictures from close to the surface, so that we can map out the best landing place for the final expedition.

Meantime, the big ships will be under construction, in the orbit of the station, but some distance away. These ships will not be designed for travel through the air, as the three-stage supply rockets must be. With no air in space, streamlining is not necessary. Two of the three ships will be designated for the round trip. The third will be designed as a cargo ship. This will be torn down on the Moon, and part of it used to build a shelter for the men there.

All three ships will have a globe at the front in which men will travel, complete with air for the journey, and with the required safety precautions. Each will also have a big platform at the rear on which banks of the rocket motors will be mounted. These motors will be the same type that are used on the regular rockets—hence, the kind with which we are familiar and which are practically in mass production. The platforms will also have legs for landing—designed to cushion the setdown and also to help level off the ship.

The passenger ships will have a network of girders between the globe and platform, and the space will be filled with fuel tanks. The cargo ship will carry stores for the expedition in its center section and will resemble a silo. It is this section that will form the huts for the explorers on the Moon.

Extra globes of fuel will be fastened outside the ships—big plastic balloons that will be drained on the takeoff and then dropped before landing.

The chief problem will be the immense amounts of fuel needed, since every drop must be carried up from Earth on the supply rockets. Largely because of this, the expedition is estimated to cost half a billion dollars, though improvements may reduce that figure. It is still much less than the cost of the station.

After our experience with the supply rockets and the station, building and using these Moon rocketships will not be too difficult a task. Once these ships are built and the crews trained, we will be facing an entirely new adventure—the setting of a course for another world, and the job of landing without air to help us.

In one way, there is no problem. We will not have to navigate blindly, as we would in a ship at sea. There will be no time when we cannot see our destination.

We cannot just aim for that destination, though, because the Moon is moving, and it will not be in the same place when the rocket comes in for the landing as it will when the ship takes off. We shall have to aim for the spot where the Moon is going to be.

Since the trip will take 5 days, that means aiming at a location on the Moon's orbit where it will be 5 days later. Astronomers have long been able to plot such a course as this, and computers will have the course worked out to the last decimal place long before the takeoff.

At zero hour, we will have to be in the most favorable spot in the orbit of the station, though. We want to make use of our speed there, without any waste.

It turns out that the best place for takeoff is at the opposite side of the Earth from our target. At that position, our orbit will just be bringing us around toward the target again. We will not be able to take off in a straight line, though. All we can do is to build up speed with our rockets and let this speed throw us slowly outward. The path becomes a great curve, as if we were moving into an orbit that kept getting farther and farther from Earth. We are still being held enough by gravity to keep turning, but the curvature becomes wider and wider as we go out.

Finally, as we reach a speed of about 19,500 miles an hour, the curve of our motion is nearly a straight line. Gravity is now very weak, and Earth slips farther and farther behind us. We are still being pulled backward, slowing as we move, but our speed is great enough to carry us finally beyond the reach of Earth.

Going slower and slower, we creep out and out. The Moon's orbit is 239,000 miles from Earth. If we could make full speed all the way, it would take us only about 12 hours to reach the Moon, but as we go slower and more and more time is needed to cover the miles, we find that the whole trip is going to take 10 times that long.

At last we are barely moving, and it seems that we are about to come to a stop, but now something else begins to influence us. The Moon at this point is almost ahead of us, having drawn toward the spot at which we are aiming. As Earth's pull on us grows weaker, the pull of the Moon grows stronger. Finally we creep across the distance where we pass from the control of Earth to that of the Moon. We cannot feel the difference, but now we are within the sphere of lunar gravity and are being pulled down by that. We begin to pick up speed, now seeming to rush down toward the surface of the satellite. We never reach the speed of takeoff, since the pull here is weaker, and since we have less distance and time for lunar gravity to operate, but as we draw closer and closer, it begins to look as if we must crash.

We have turned by this time, reversing our ships so the rockets point down to the Moon. At a height of exactly 600 miles, the blast cuts on. At first it will seem as if our speed has not changed at all, though the heavy acceleration will prove that the

rockets are working. (That acceleration, incidentally, will not have to be nearly so high as it is in the three-stage supply rockets.)

The distance will decrease frighteningly, and we will begin to see the spot on the Moon which our maps show to be our landing site. Then the rockets will blast forward to overcome the speed of the ship. The surface will still seem to rush at us. Now for the first time our pilots will have the formidable job of landing by rocket power without any other means of cushioning the landing. The pilots will have to bring their ships to zero speed at exactly the split second when the legs touch the surface.

To make matters worse, visibility will not exist. The blast from the rockets will make it impossible to see the surface. The men guiding the ships will have to judge height by means of radio instruments. They had better hope that the first choice of landing spot (made during the initial survey) was correct, and that the surface is fairly even.

It will not be so dangerous as it sounds, however. The electronic instruments are actually more precise than vision in estimating distance and speed. The surface will have been studied carefully through the telescope at the station and from the pictures taken on the exploratory trip. Even if the pilot misjudges a trifle, such an error will not be serious.

There will be a feeler leg projecting downward and, as it touches the surface, it will cut off the blast automatically at the right time. The shock-absorbing power of the other legs, plus the fact that the gravity on the Moon is so low, will smooth out quite a bit of minor miscalculations at the last second.

Once the ships have landed, there will be a period of high activity while the supply rocket is stripped of the center section, each half of which will be erected in a safe place for housing the people. The power and radar devices will be mounted for use by the expedition. The food and other supplies will be moved into storage, and the fuel remaining in the tanks of the supply ship will be transferred to the other ships for the return journey. Almost nothing of the supply rocket will be wasted, except the rocket motors.

To make the handling of all the supplies a smooth operation, there will be small tractors mounted on caterpillar treads. These tractors will be powered by the same hydrogen-peroxide method of running a steam turbine as that which powers the pumps for the rocket fuel. Since the Moon has no air—at least, not enough to be of any use—the tractors will have to depend on something of this type.

At the end of the six weeks, when the Moon is in a favorable position for the return trip, the two passenger ships will be made ready for the voyage back. The shelters, the power equipment that came from the cargo ship, and the radar antennae will be left behind, along with the tractors and everything not needed for the return. This will make the next trip simpler, and will make it possible to build up a bigger and better base on the Moon.

In many ways, the return trip will be the reverse of the voyage out to the Moon. The ships will rise from the surface and accelerate to a high enough speed to pass over into the area where the pull of the Earth will begin speeding them up in the long fall back toward the station. Again, five days will be necessary for the trip. At the end of that time, the two returning ships will head around the opposite side of the Earth from which they started. Their rockets will be blasting forward to slow their speed to that of the station.

This time, the curve of their path around the Earth will grow tighter and tighter, until they have matched their original speed and orbit. There the ships can wait for refueling and the next voyage—a much cheaper voyage, but still one that requires vast amounts of fuel.

Incidentally, there is one disadvantage to the orbit of the station as it circles from over one pole to over the other. This is the reason why the ships must take off to and from the Moon at only specific times. (Scientists have decided that a transpolar orbit will prove somewhat more stable than one around the equator.)

You can visualize this easily by imagining a tiny ball circling around the poles of a model globe. Now imagine the Moon as another globe in a circle farther out, but around the equator.

Obviously, if the little sphere were to shoot out from its orbit, there are only two spots on the orbit of the Moon which it could hit; therefore, since the Moon takes four weeks to circle the Earth, this means that the trips must be calculated in terms of the two-week periods between these two points on the Moon's orbit.

However, for a long time to come, the delay of at least two weeks between trips will not be anything to worry about. Unless our exploration of the surface of the satellite reveals something beyond our imagination, it will be a long, long time before more frequent trips are required!

CHAPTER 12

another world

One of the rules of both science and common experience is that you cannot learn much from one example. If you tried to find out everything about dogs from only one animal, you might get some very false ideas. Too much would depend on accidental choice of the dog. You might decide that all dogs were vicious, disloyal and surly, if one dog behaved that way. The present picture of the class of animals known as dogs has come from thousands of years and millions of examples—and even now, no one fully understands everything about dogs.

When it comes to studying worlds in space, however, we have had to learn almost everything we know about them from one example! The only world we have been able to reach is Earth!

We have looked at other worlds through telescopes. But the best view we have of the Moon—the nearest of all other worlds—has been distorted by irregularities in our atmosphere, and what we see always looks as if we were still quite a distance away from the surface.

Also, when we try to study the surface by other instruments—such as *spectroscopes* that break the light down in ways which enable us to find what substances reflected the light—we are not really seeing the true light that was started toward us. Instead, we are seeing that light only after it has passed through the air, which filters out some of the original. This makes getting a real picture of any other world very difficult. We still have not found out for sure whether the mysterious "canals" of Mars really exist, and we know almost nothing about Venus because of the blanket of clouds around that planet.

When we have an observatory out in space, some of the questions will be cleared up. We will still be studying the worlds from a distance, though, and much of what we learn will be mixed with guesses.

Because of that, it is very important to us to make an actual study of some other world. By comparing what has happened there with what we have learned about our own world, we will know much more about both planets! Perhaps we will even find better ways of learning just how old our own planet really is, for instance.

The Moon is going to be much different from Earth, but those differences are going to help us.

Some of the differences are known to us already, though we cannot be sure of all the details. We know enough to equip our first expedition with the tools the explorers will need, and from those men we will learn a great deal more.

The expedition will not be like most exploring teams. It will not be looking for daring adventure or things to photograph as novelties. The explorers cannot avoid finding both of those, but the less danger and adventure they meet, the better they will like it. This group will be a team of scientific men and women, carefully chosen to learn as much of the basic facts about our nearest neighbor in space as can be discovered in six weeks. They will collect samples, run tests, take scientific and mapping photographs, and write detailed reports. The real study will probably be made after they return, by many other scientists working with the material the members of the expedition discover.

Using the tractors, the men will move out carefully from their permanent headquarters. The crater or plain on which they make the initial landing will be one picked to place them where most of the biggest mysteries of the Moon will not be too far away.

We can tell some of the things which they will find, and we know many of the questions they will want to answer.

The explorers will find a world without air, or so little air that it cannot be detected from Earth. There may be some faint wisps; some astronomers have reported that meteorites have been seen to glow when approaching the surface of the satellite. If so, it still does not mean that there is any air that we could detect when standing on the surface. Gravity is weak, which has permitted great high mountains to be thrown up, and in a world without air or water there is no great erosion to wear these peaks smooth.

Everything will be harsh and rugged. Cracks will be sharp and severe. No wind will have moved light material into the hollows, to level the surface. The light will be like that in space—glaring upon exposed surfaces and giving inky-black shadows. It may be reflected from some surfaces into the darker places, so that it will not always be absolute light and complete dark, but there cannot be the softness of diffused light. On Earth the dust in the air is enough to spread some light everywhere in daytime, but dust is lacking on the Moon.

There are great ranges of mountains, and great plains that look flat from Earth. Most of these flat sections are named "seas" in maps of the Moon. The use of that word has long since proved to be a mistake. We know there is no water there, because it would all have evaporated out into space, long ago. Probably there never was water or air. The Moon was too light to hold hydrogen or oxygen—or any of the other light gases—even when it was being formed.

Our explorers will land somewhere near one of the lunar poles, to avoid the terrible heat of the full Sun on the rocks of the surface at lunar midday. (Naturally, since the surface bends away from the Sun at the poles, the sunlight there is spread out over more territory, and gives less heat for each square mile, just as it does at the poles of Earth.) At the equator of the Moon, when the Sun is beaming straight down, the surface may reach a temperature far above that of boiling water. At midnight, on the surface, those same rocks may be hundreds of degrees below zero.

Space, even on the Moon, will not carry heat well, but the rocks will carry the heat which will penetrate the feet and equipment of the explorers, so they will try to avoid any section that will reach too high a temperature.

They will almost certainly not land on the side of the Moon opposite Earth. We all know that the Moon always turns the same face toward Earth and that nobody has ever seen the other side. Once this led to fanciful ideas that there might be a great hollow there, where air could collect and where life could exist. Now we know better—any such hollow would have an effect on the pulls that exist between Earth and the Moon, and its depth could be estimated.

We can be reasonably sure the other side of the Moon is about the same as the one we see. From ships in space, photographs for study will be made of the other side, and someday we will want to explore it. On the first trip to the Moon, though, we will choose a place from which we can see Earth, because radio beams in space will not turn around corners, and we can only keep in contact by staying in sight of Earth.

Also, we know this side, and we know where to look for the answers to some of the questions concerning the Moon. We will learn more by sticking to familiar ground.

One puzzle to be solved is the cause of the great craters we see. The Moon is pitted with them—great circular rings, sometimes with rings inside rings. Originally, these craters were thought to have been caused by lava rings thrust up by volcanoes. Many of the English astronomers still believe this theory. The American scientists, on the other hand, feel that this belief does not fit what they see.

Most of the Americans believe that the craters were caused by meteorites striking the surface long ago (when there were more meteorites, and bigger ones, probably; after all, each one that strikes means there is one less left). If you can get a box of soft dust—or even flour—and drop a small pebble into it from above, you will soon find that you can make holes that look just like the lunar craters.

We will not be sure of the cause, however, until we can reach the Moon and find out what substances are present there. If the material on the surface is volcanic, then the lava will prove it. If not, and the surface is of a soft enough matter, then it might be meteoric in origin. If none of our theories work, we will still be ahead, because we will have learned what not to believe.

There are also the great rays. On the surface of the Moon, we can see great white lines that travel for hundreds of miles in straight lines, through mountain ranges and over plains, usually with several of them radiating from some central spot. Nobody has a good explanation of those lines that satisfies most astronomers, and we very much want to know what they are.

We are also puzzled by the very brightness of the Moon. When the Sun shines on it, it reflects more light back to us than most objects should. Seen from the Moon, the Earth will be much bigger, of course, but probably not so bright. This *albedo,* or power of reflection, has long been a mystery.

One suggestion has been that the Moon is covered with a layer of gypsum in most places. *Gypsum* is like plaster of Paris after it has set. It is a light, soft rock with a very white color that would reflect a great amount of light.

If the covering is gypsum, we are in luck in one way. Gypsum contains a good deal of water. It is not water that is merely absorbed, but rather actually locked into the crystals chemically, as it is in a plaster of Paris statuette. Such water can be baked out, though, without using too much heat, and then collected.

Then it would be possible to get all the water needed for our people on the Moon right from its surface. We can free oxygen from the water, by passing an electric current through it. We get two parts of hydrogen—which we could let escape into space, or save for other uses—and one of oxygen. With the full sunlight on the Moon, we could set up solar furnaces and boilers and generate all the power we would need.

This would also enable us to power rockets from material found on the Moon. Hydrogen and oxygen must be in liquid form for use in the fuel, but they could be liquefied easily during the cold lunar night, and stored in caves out of the sunlight. The two elements are much harder to handle in rockets than hydrazine and nitric acid. Still, if we could produce hydrogen and oxygen on the Moon, instead of having to carry enough fuel for the return trip, it would make things much easier in the long run, and we would certainly find ways to use them.

We do not know that what we see is gypsum, however.

We may, on the other hand, find all sorts of minerals. Some may be in quite different form from what they are on Earth, since conditions on the Moon are so unlike the ones on our world.

Probably the explorers on the first trip will not find anything in terms of market value to bring back, and we will almost certainly never be shipping much from the Moon. The cost of shipping would be so high that very few things would be worth the price. Gold already mined and lying in bars on the surface of the Moon would not be worth moving back. Diamonds might, but it is doubtful; much of the value of a diamond comes from the cutting and from its rarity. If uncut diamonds became common, they would have very little value.

We might even find life on the Moon. The chances are not too good, and such life would not be intelligent or even animal life. The most we could hope for would be a very crude, very low form, like some of the lichens on Earth, or perhaps even lower types. Nevertheless, we do have some evidence which suggests there may be traces of life there.

We have seen some strange changes in color in a few of the craters. This change in color on the Moon takes place as the Sun rises, and then changes back at night. It is hard to explain the phenomenon in any way except by thinking that some crude, thin layer of plant life grows up and shrinks back. In that case, there is reason to believe a very thin wisp of air might be in the craters.

This possibility is worth investigating, though it may turn out to be only some strange crystal which behaves oddly under the heat of the Sun. We do not know of any substance which would behave like that, but we are not on the Moon, where strange conditions do exist.

While the scientists are studying the Moon, they will also be looking for opportunities to live there comfortably. They know that it will take years and years of study to learn all we want to know about the Moon, and that it will be hard to make frequent trips there. They will hope to find ways of setting up a colony that will be almost self-sufficient, with the inhabitants able to live and study on the Moon with only occasional trips to and from Earth.

Such a feat is not impossible, either. Dwellings can be dug out of the rock below the surface and cemented with some airtight substance. Carefully arranged "hothouses," for hydroponic growth of plants in tanks of water, can be built to provide clean, fresh air and to produce most of the food the people will need. Power can come from the Sun, though a way must be found to store this energy for use during the long two weeks of night.

They may not find the gypsum mentioned earlier, though doing so would simplify things, but they certainly will find minerals that contain most of the necessary elements. Rocks that contain nitrides for nitrogen, oxides for oxygen, hydrates for hydrogen, and carbides or carbonates for carbon are common. These four elements are the building blocks of most life and of both hydrazine and nitric acid. With the addition of some phosphorus, calcium, iron, and a few other traces of elements, the settlers could create the fertilizer for their plants. Aluminum or some other metal might be produced. The material of the Moon is much lighter than that of Earth, so there would not be much hope of finding a rich deposit of uranium. Still, with time and much work, a colony could be set up that would need very few supplies it could not produce.

If such a colony were established, space travel would be much easier. Ships could be refueled from the Moon, and the rockets would not even have to land after they arrived; they could go into an orbit about the Moon, and local supply rockets could go up to transship supplies.

With such a happy arrangement, even the small final stages of the ships supplying the first station could make the trip, refuel and return. Travel between the station and the Moon might even be much cheaper and easier than trips between Earth and the station.

A colony such as I have described would be made up of scientists studying the Moon as well as some military men perhaps. Whether there would ever be anything on the Moon to make it possible for men to move there to live without military or scientific need we cannot say yet. There is no evidence at present that anything on the Moon (except knowledge) would be profitable to men.

Such evidence will not be found until we get there, or even later. Men have done many things which appeared to offer no profit, only to find that some development made them of the greatest value. When a way was found to purify uranium, it seemed that the company doing the work would never get any return for its effort. Years later, it turned out to be an immensely valuable patent—and the change came about through a discovery made by scientists who were looking for pure knowledge. It is never safe to say that anything is useless.

SECTION IV

other planets

CHAPTER 13

paths to the planets

MEN are not going to be content to stop exploring space after they have reached the Moon. There are other puzzles that they want to solve, and Mars is one of the biggest of these. It is also more valuable to us in finding out about planets like Earth, since it resembles Earth more closely than any other planet, especially much more closely than the Moon.

Another reason for wanting to go beyond the Moon is even simpler—men hate to face a challenge and do nothing about it. Mount Everest has been climbed, and the Moon will be reached. After that, thoughts are going to turn to the other worlds circling the Sun.

In fact, after Dr. von Braun had figured how we could build a station in space and then get to the Moon, he plunged into the problem of reaching Mars. He admits that his methods for reaching Mars will undoubtedly be greatly improved on in the actual trip, but he had to see whether it could be done, even without improvements.

He found it was possible, but then his scientific caution arose to prevent too much enthusiasm. Yes, it could be done, but it would not be done in our time. It probably would not be done until another 100 years or more had passed—sometime in 2050 or later. . . .

With all respect to Dr. von Braun, I cannot help believing the trip will be made sooner. I remember an article I read in 1925 by a very famous airplane designer who was building some of the greatest planes of the day.

In the article, he proposed some wild ideas that most of the airplane engineers regarded as fantastic. He predicted that in another 50 or 60 years, men would be able to fly at a speed of as high as 500 miles an hour and to cross the country in 10 hours or less. When asked about greater speeds, he shook his head—he doubted whether we would be able to go as fast as the speed of sound, even in another 100 years, if at all.

He was ahead of his time, but he was terribly wrong in his guess about the number of years! Fifteen years later, men were already surpassing the speeds he had mentioned. Twenty years later, they were ready to break the sound barrier and reach speeds of over 700 miles an hour. Commercial planes were flying coast to coast regularly in about 10 hours.

Except for new developments necessary to attain supersonic speeds, no really great new ideas were needed to build those commercial planes. There were just steady improvements, but ones which came much faster than the designer could have believed.

I feel that Dr. von Braun is right in being cautious, because no scientist can be rash and make wild guesses; he has to stick to what he can work out logically. But I also feel we will begin our first real interplanetary flight (probably to Mars) much sooner than Von Braun believes, because men are not always logical when they start research on new ideas. Things have a habit of speeding up remarkably after the first work in any field is done. Dr. von Braun's own work with rockets is good proof of that theory.

However, let us not get too hopeful for an early trip to Mars. The planets are much farther away than the Moon. Instead of thousands of miles from Earth, they lie millions of miles away. In addition, the courses that ships must take to reach the planets are much greater than the actual distance these other worlds are from Earth.

In fact, when we move from planet to planet, we have to start thinking in new ways about the best means to get somewhere. We cannot just sight along Mars' orbit to the nearest point and then set out in a fairly straight line to reach it. We would be required to build up very high speeds and burn huge amounts of fuel.

Maybe in the future, some fantastic new fuel will make it possible. Right now we are trying to deal with the facts we know, and not go off into wild hopes. We have to continue working with hydrazine and nitric acid, until we can find a better fuel. This means that instead of a direct route we must choose the path to the planets which will use the smallest quantity of fuel.

That, again, means that we must make the fullest use of all the speed we already have. The Earth has no speed at all outward toward Mars. To take off straight toward the nearest point on the orbit of the fourth planet would mean that every bit of speed would have to come from our fuel.

On the other hand, Earth is moving at a speed of 18 miles a second around the Sun. A space station at a height of 1,000 miles from the surface will be moving at more than 4 miles a second, which rate can be added to the speed of Earth to give us a total speed of about 23 miles a second. Now if we could add only a few more miles a second of speed, we would be able to go surprising distances.

For example, by adding less than 4 miles a second to our speed, we would move out away from Earth until we reached the orbit of Mars. A total speed of 27 miles a second sounds like a high figure, but we have picked most of it up for free, so to speak, by using that which was already in existence.

The reason for our moving outward, properly speaking, is that this increase in speed has increased our resistance to a change in direction—or has given us more centrifugal force. Our rocketship moves outward from the station and from Earth, forced farther from the Sun because it has more inertia, or resistance to being pulled into a tight circle, than Earth.

As the rocketship rises away from the Sun, it is slowed by the Sun's huge field of gravity. Earth has long ago moved so far from us that the planet's gravity does not matter now. We go on coasting out, using up the extra energy in rising from the Sun, until we can strike a new balance. That new balance between inertia and solar gravity turns out to be in the orbit of Mars.

If we want to reach Venus, the best way is to take off when the station's speed can be subtracted from that of Earth—in other words, when the motion of the station is in the opposite direction from Earth's swing around the Sun. Then we use the rocket power to lose still more speed, and begin falling back and downward. The Sun is now pulling at us, increasing our speed, until we again find a point of balance in the orbit of Venus.

These trips are going to be very long ones, both in time and in the amount of space covered. We do not just travel the difference in distance from the Sun between the planets; we make a long, slow curve around the Sun. By the time we finish our trip, we shall be on the other side of the Sun from the point where we started.

There is a fairly simple way of drawing pictures of the best orbits between planets, and one which requires no complicated figuring. Such a diagram will give us a reasonably accurate orbit for our trip, too.

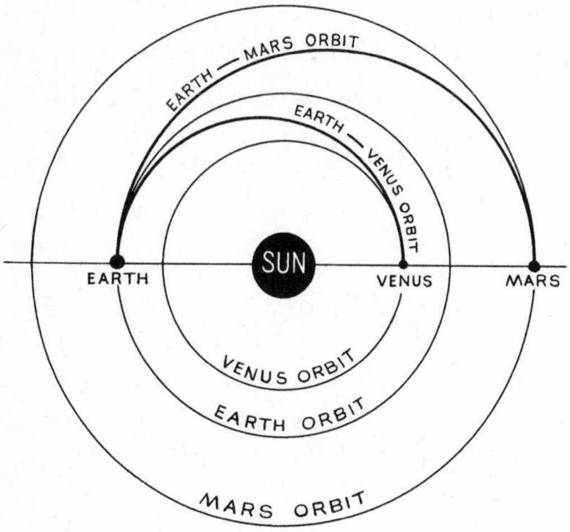

On a piece of paper, make a mark for the Sun and use that as a center point. Now, with a compass, draw circles for the orbits of Earth and the other planets. Venus should have a circle with a diameter a trifle less than $3/4$ that of Earth, and Mars should be given an orbit with a diameter just a trifle more than $1\frac{1}{2}$ that of Earth.

Next lay a ruler across the "Sun" and mark out spots wherever the ruler crosses an orbit. This gives one set of spots for each orbit on one side of the Sun (as we shall still call the center of our circles), and another set on the other side of the Sun.

Then, to find the orbit between any two planets, select the spot on one side of the Sun for one planet and on the other side of the Sun for the other. These will be our takeoff and landing points.

The orbit of our ship can be shown by the smallest circle which we can fit over these two points. You might try various can tops, saucers or anything else round in shape, if you want to try it, and experiment until you find one that will barely touch both spots.

A line drawn between these two spots along that circle will be very close to a true orbit for our spaceship.

Of course, the orbit will not be perfect, since the real paths of the planets do not form perfect circles, and since there will be some bending of the ship's path as a result of the gravity of the two planets. It is accurate enough for any reasonable-sized circles we care to draw. In fact, if a perfect picture of such an orbit were drawn beside the rough one, we would have a hard time seeing the difference.

That method seems like a very long way around, but it will be the most economical one we can find for the trip. Shortening the orbit will result in huge increases in the amount of fuel we will need, both for takeoff and landing. By using the orbits we have just described, the spaceship not only saves fuel in making the trip, but it will arrive at a speed not too greatly different from that of the planet, and it will be heading in the same direction. Those points are very important matters to consider.

This procedure creates another problem. Now we cannot take off whenever we wish. If we did, we would likely arrive at the orbit of the planet we have chosen and find that planet somewhere else. Then all our work would be for nothing. It would not be as bad as it sounds, though, since we would not be lost forever in space. We would simply go right around the circle we started to draw and arrive at Earth's orbit again, but now Earth probably would not be there!

We will have to plan our trip at those times when the planet we want to reach will be exactly opposite our takeoff point, after allowing for the number of days the whole trip will take. Then, if we want to land, stay awhile and return home later, we will have to wait until the Earth is opposite the takeoff point from the planet we are visiting. Here again we must allow for the time the return trip will take.

It gets to be a problem for the big calculating machines. Men can figure it out by hand, but it would take too long, so before we decide to go, we shall let the calculating machines give us a set of workable orbits for the correct dates, and another set for our return. We will choose the ones that look best, and then we will follow them exactly.

We cannot be completely accurate in all our maneuvers, though we will try to be as close as we can. We may have to make some corrections in our course. At this point we run into a problem that did not really exist on the simple trip to the Moon. Now we cannot see our destination at all, because it is on the other side of the Sun. It would not help too much even if we did, since we are not going to be traveling anywhere near a straight line in our flight. If we have to know exactly where we are and how well we are doing, we will need some way to navigate.

Compasses will not work in space, of a certainty. There is no handy North Pole in space, and the Earth's poles will be far away.

We will have to go back to the old way of navigating by the stars, with one added difficulty—now we must navigate up and down as well as in the other directions.

This will be entirely possible to do, however. We will have tables worked out, just as the navigators on ships do. These will give us an exact fix in space in terms of the position of certain bright and easily seen stars. Since the stars are so far away, the distance traveled between planets will not seem to change the direction of those stars enough to matter.

We will read the positions on special instruments (like those used by ship navigators), while looking at those stars. Then we will check our tables and use the figures there to locate exactly where we are. The same tables will show the positions of all the planets at any time, and we can quickly see whether we are on course or not. By making several readings and finding how much distance we have covered in a certain length of time, we can quickly determine our speed.

From that we can draw our orbit on the charts carried with us, and we will be absolutely sure of how we are doing.

In the spaceships, we will have one advantage over the seamen, too. There is never any bad weather in space. The stars will be visible all the time, ready for us to use them whenever necessary. There is no chance of our getting lost. Also, we will not have to contend with uncertain winds and tides that might throw us off course. The gravity pull from the Sun and planets will have an effect on our flight, but they will be constant in direction and force for any position. We will be able to predict exactly what effect they will have on us at any given point in space and at any given time.

The work will be complicated, but the real task will be done by the computing machines. They will work out the tables and charts, and once we have those, we will find them fairly easy to follow.

To make it still simpler, we usually will not move much in one direction. The planets all go around the Sun in one flat plane. If we call the Sun's poles up and down, and its equator the plane of the planets, then we will not have any reason to go up or down much. We will just move around on the plane of the planets.

This method is not just a rough idea, either. The whole business of navigating in space has been considered very carefully by astronomers, and the way has been worked out well enough so that the tables and charts could be drawn up in a very short time, if we needed them.

There is not much question about being able to add the necessary speed by rocket power, either. We will have to gain more speed to get from Earth to the station than we will need to move from the station to either Mars or Venus. In fact, it is one of the basic oddities of space travel that going up the first 1,000 miles to the station is going to require more fuel than will be required for any other trip we will make for a long time afterward, even though we decide to travel millions of miles beyond the station.

CHAPTER 14

mars

EVERYONE has heard of the Martian "canals." Long before anyone was sure that we could ever travel in space, there was a terrific amount of excitement at the announcement that the fourth planet had such canals. To the average person, this could only mean that there was intelligent life on the planet, and all sorts of fantastic schemes were thought up to signal the Martians.

It was all a misunderstanding, however. An astronomer named Giovanni Schiaparelli reported seeing certain markings on Mars in 1877. He was Italian, and he used the Italian word *canali* to describe what these markings looked like—meaning channels, not canals. The word was translated as "canals," which are artificial things, and the confusion spread before it could be checked.

Even some of the astronomers, however, were convinced that the markings showed intelligent life. Dr. Percival Lowell mapped these straight lines carefully and felt certain that they proved there was such intelligence on Mars.

Other astronomers have been unable to see the markings at all! Some see them; some do not. So far, photography does not give us a sure answer. The trouble seems to be that the markings show up better in small telescopes than in the large ones, but photography is at its best only when it can have the light-gathering power of one of the larger telescopes.

We have some evidence that there are such markings. Several men have produced photographs that show them faintly, but there is not enough proof one way or the other yet to be certain.

Fortunately, we have hopes of finding the explanation soon. In 1956, Mars was about 35 million miles from us—which is a very close approach for that planet. That nearness of the planet enabled us to try our latest photographic tricks, and we may have the answer from those pictures.

By the time we get into space, with no blur caused by atmosphere, we will know, at least, whether or not there are markings. We still will not know what those strange markings are, however. We do not believe they show intelligence now, even if they exist, but we may have to go to Mars to prove that they do not indicate some form of intelligent life.

Even if there are no "canals," we will still want to make the journey to Mars, because we are reasonably sure that the planet has life of some kind. There are changes of color with the seasons, and variations from year to year that can only be explained fully by thinking that plants of some kind are growing there. Any biologist on Earth would give almost anything for an opportunity to study such plants from another world.

Also, Mars is more like Earth than any other world we can see. It has some air—very little—but it is completely unfit for breathing by Earthmen. There is evidence of traces of water, and the temperatures, while extreme from our point of view, are still within a range we could tolerate.

Without question, the first planet we will try to visit will be Mars.

This time, we are facing a much more difficult task than we had getting to the Moon. Those orbits we looked at earlier show that the trip to Mars will have to be a long one. Even though Mars and Earth sometimes come as close together as they did in 1956 (and will again in 1971), the trip in one direction will cover about 350 million miles and will take 258 days—more than 8 months! Then when we add the time the men will have to stay on Mars before they can start back, and the length of time of the return trip, we find they will be gone more than 2½ years!

Such a long trip requires huge supplies of food, water, air and other materials, plus all the equipment needed to live on an unknown world. To make matters worse, the explorers will not even be able to use the transpolar space station for the takeoff. They will have to be in an orbit that is on the same plane as the planets—roughly, around the Earth's equator—in order to use the speed of that orbit in the direction they must go. They will either have to build a special station or find a way to construct their ships in space without the need of a full station.

Dr. von Braun's plans are not as certain for the journey to Mars as they were for the earlier trips. He worked the plans out in complete detail, but added a warning that by the time of this flight there may well be major changes made. In fact, he has suggested some changes in his original plans.

According to his original calculations, we shall need 10 ships to carry cargo, fuel for landing and return, and the exploration crew. There will be quite a few more men needed for the Mars trip than for the Moon trip, too. These ships will look much like the cargo ship for the Moon voyage, except that three of them will have the globes for living quarters replaced by winged, streamlined sections like the final stages on the supply ships for the station—though these new ones will be considerably larger.

The start of the trip will be similar to the one to the Moon, except that it will be from around the equator instead of around the poles. The 10 ships will accelerate to the needed speed of about 27 miles a second—that is, 4 miles a second faster than that which the ships had traveled in their orbit around Earth. By the time the ships are nearly 6,000 miles out from the surface of Earth, they will have achieved this speed. Then they will coast the rest of the way, during all the 8 months of the trip.

When the ships reach Mars, they will go into an orbit about 600 miles above the surface of the planet. Here the three streamlined ships will take on the men who are to go the rest of the way. These ships will go down by using the thin air of Mars, much as the returning final stage of a rocket lands on Earth. Other trips to and from the 600-mile orbit will be made in these smaller ships, and the main body of the expedition will remain waiting above, to save fuel.

Then, for about a year, the people of the expedition will be busy gathering all the facts they can about our neighbor in the skies. The exploration will be hard, rough work, too.

The air on Mars is much thinner than that at the top of Mount Everest and totally unfit for men to breathe. There is some water on Mars, since we see it form a deposit at the poles every winter, but there can be only a very small amount. At most, the water can form icecaps that are only inches thick. The air will be *dry,* and there will probably be no sign of water in liquid form that the men can find.

Most of the planet Mars is probably a sandy wasteland, not unlike some of our deserts. There are no mountains, and the hills must be rounded by erosion. Even the thin air can create severe storms, since we can see these disturbances in our telescopes. Fine dust will be blown about, though the terrible sandstorms of fiction are probably exaggerated. Even against the gravity of Mars—which is only about three-eighths that of Earth—such thin air could hardly lift any great amount of heavy sand, unless the winds traveled at even higher velocities than we have seen.

Mars has a day only a few minutes longer than that of Earth. This period of rotation and the atmosphere keep the temperature from being so extreme as that of the Moon, but it still is hardly well-designed for human comfort. At midday near the equator, it grows fairly warm—probably 80 or 85 degrees above zero on our thermometers. As the Sun goes down, the temperature drops rapidly. By midnight, it will reach almost 100 degrees below zero!

How living plants can stand such a low temperature is something of a mystery. We have some plants on Earth that can grow in the ice of the Far North, but none that could stand the extremes of temperature on Mars. There must be some means for the plant life there to insulate itself at night, probably by drawing up into small balls with a furry fuzz on the outside, though we can only make a guess about that.

Unless we are very much mistaken, however, there is plant life on Mars. It may be a very low level of such life, but it covers great sections of the planet.

With the small quantities of water available, plant life must seem more dead than alive. Even cactus on Earth has much water stored in it, and there seems to be very little chance for plants on Mars to find that much water. They must be terribly dry. Perhaps that helps them to stand the severe cold at night, since they would contain practically no moisture which would freeze.

This plant life is going to receive attention from the men exploring the planet, at any rate. It is not likely that we will obtain any usable drugs from the plants—their chemistry will be much like that of Earth plants in some ways, but it will be different enough to make them almost certainly useless to us, as well as hopelessly inedible. Still, they will help to teach us a great deal about the development of life.

If the telescope in the space station shows us that there are canals—or whatever the marks may be—these will also be explored carefully. Nobody at the present time can make even an intelligent guess as to what they really are. In fiction, I have tried to give some logical answer, and have found at least one solution* that just might explain the canals without their having been made by intelligent life. Such guesses are based on no facts at all.

Whatever the plants are, we can reasonably assume they are some natural phenomenon of Nature peculiar to Mars, or else the product of some plant growth and action.

Almost surely, our explorers will find no higher animal life of any kind. Most scientists believe there will be no animal life at all on Mars. We cannot be completely positive of this. We can find no sign of oxygen

* See *Marooned on Mars,* by Lester del Rey.

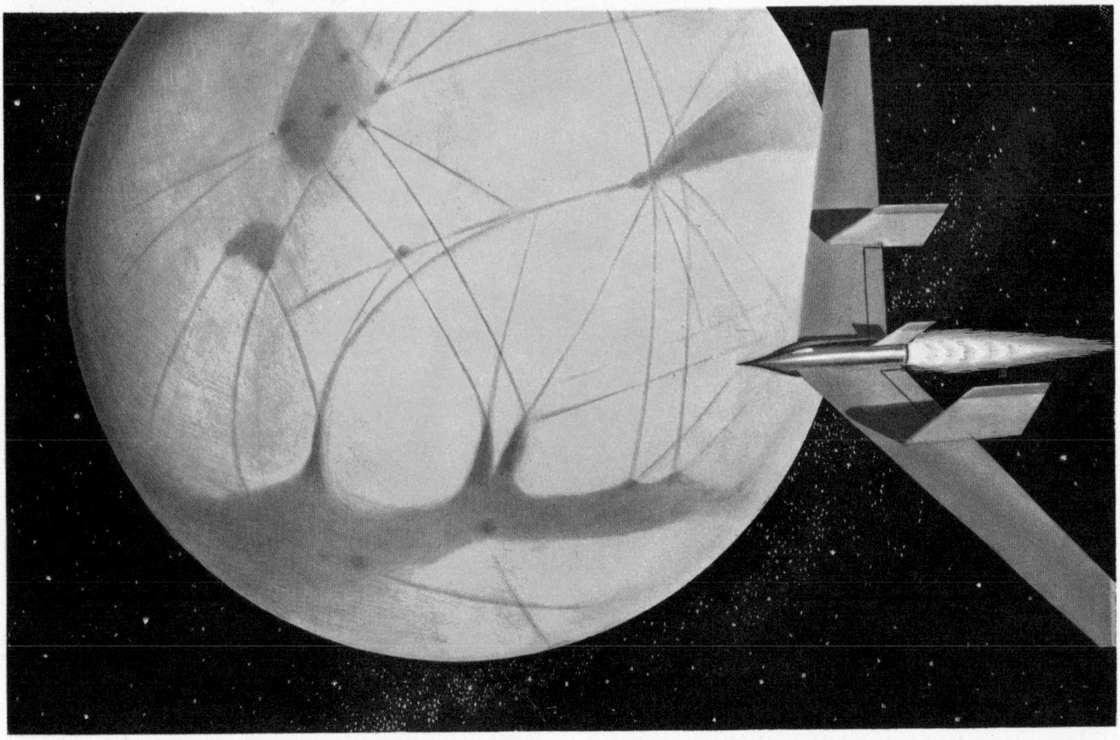

in the air of Mars, but this is no sure proof, since it is very difficult to study the atmosphere of another planet through the thick blanket of our own air. Certainly, however, there can be very little oxygen for an animal to breathe. With such a slim prospect of being able to burn the food in its body by the aid of oxygen breathed in, any animal there would make a snail look like greased lightning. It would live so slowly that we might mistake it for a rock rather than something alive.

The chances of finding anything as intelligent as a toad or a very stupid bird are very dim indeed. When we talk about finding living things intelligent enough to build dwellings, use tools and learn to talk with us, we are only wishing hopefully. Such life could not survive on Mars.

There is always the objection that Martian life might not work like ours. It might have a different basis; it might not even need oxygen and water.

There is no good answer to that theory, because we know nothing about any kind of life except our own. Chemists and biologists have to admit that there could be other ways of developing life, perhaps; but when all the facts are examined, those ways seem quite doubtful. Still, perhaps some of them would work.

We cannot say there could not be other types of life, though we certainly cannot expect it. Even then, it is hard to see how we could have really civilized Martians with complicated tools. No fire could burn on Mars because of the atmosphere; without fire, it is impossible to begin smelting metals for civilization. (True, we can use plastics and other materials, but we could not have the plastics unless we had the metals first. We could not have learned how to refine some metals, such as aluminum, without fire, unless we had had the fire first.)

There is one other fact that is somewhat against the "different form of life" theory.

From what we can see in our telescopes, the life on Mars seems to operate with something very much like Earth's chlorophyll. A number of different checks on this belief give the same result. It seems logical that life similar enough to us to use the same basic chemistry as our own plants would be similar in much of the rest of its body chemistry.

The explorers who first visit Mars are going to have a busy year. They will have no time to watch the two moons of the planet—Phobos and Deimos—racing across the sky, as so many heroes of fiction seem to do. Those tiny bodies of airless rock, only a few miles in diameter, would be barely visible from the surface of Mars, and would not be as well worth watching as would any of the brighter stars.

When the Sun goes down, the men will retreat from the cold to portable dwellings, or at least be sure to stay inside the cabs of the tractors that they will use to carry them about the surface. During the daytime, they will be fully occupied trying to understand all the puzzles and peculiarities they are sure to find.

At the end of the year on Mars, the rockets will drop down for the last time to take on the explorers and their discoveries. Much of their equipment will be left behind to save weight.

Mars is only about half as large as Earth, and its gravity is less of a problem. It will still take a great deal of fuel to make the trip back to the station, where landing will take as much power as the original takeoff. It is a reliable rule that speed lost in going one way in an orbit will be regained in going the other way.

The cargo and supplies for the return trip will probably be placed in fewer of the big rockets than were used for the trip to Mars. Since most of the supplies will have been used up in 20 months' time, much less space will be required for what is left. Fuel will be shifted to the ships that are to return, and everything will be double checked.

When the time is exactly on schedule, the ships will blast away, slowing by rocket power until they drift away from Mars. Then for 8 more months they will drift back around the Sun, moving slowly inward to Earth's orbit and gaining speed, until Earth is approaching and they can again maneuver back into the orbit which they left.

No writer could possibly do justice to the story the explorers will have to tell of the long voyage. Sometimes I wish I could have been born late enough to have some hope of reading the account of those first men on Mars. Unfortunately, I cannot convince myself that such a trip can be made in my lifetime.

However, Dr. von Braun has suggested changes in his original plans which may shorten the time we must wait for the exploration of Mars. The new plans call for only 2 ships and 12 men to make the trip and a more complicated method of arriving back in an orbit around Earth has been evolved. With a crew as small as this, naturally a less thorough investigation of our neighboring world would result, but it might be wise to sacrifice some details in order to shorten the time we must wait for the trip to take place.

I would not be surprised if quite a few people who read this volume do live to read the story of our first visit to Mars. I am sure that the reality will be much more thrilling than anything fiction has to offer.

CHAPTER 15

other frontiers

Once we have explored Mars, it would seem natural for us to turn to the other worlds that revolve around the Sun. Venus will be the logical goal for the next trip through space, and it should not be too hard to get there. After all, that planet is closer to Earth than Mars, and it has an even thicker atmosphere to help us land.

Almost certainly we will visit Venus next, but the trip will be more difficult than it seems, because we do not yet know enough about the planet to make detailed plans. For the trip to Mars, we could design the types of shelter and clothing needed, and we would know that the men who landed there would find no difficulty in moving about on the surface. The same is not true of Venus.

Even though Venus is our closest neighbor in space (except for our Moon), the planet remains a great mystery. We know that it is almost the same size as Earth, and that its gravity is also much like that of our own world. We know that it revolves around the Sun once each 225 of our days, and that it has a fairly thick atmosphere. Beyond these facts, we know almost nothing.

When we look at Venus through the telescope, we see nothing but a shining globe of white. This globe is the upper layer of its atmosphere, and the whiteness is caused by clouds of some kind that completely cover the planet. We cannot yet see through this layer to learn about the surface of the world beneath.

We do not even know how long the day is on Venus, though most astronomers believe it is quite a bit longer than 24 hours. There must be a day and a night on the planet. If it did not rotate on its axis, but always turned the same side toward the Sun, all the air would condense on the cold side and eventually freeze there, leaving an airless world. The longer the day, the greater difference in temperature there would be between the hot and cold sides of the planet. By using delicate instruments, we have measured the temperatures; the results make us think that the day on Venus is somewhere between 10 and 20 times as long as ours.

The clouds suggest that Venus may have large quantities of water and that there may be air there which we can breathe. Also, while the planet is closer to the Sun and would be much hotter than Earth, the temperature near the poles should be quite comfortable for us, and the atmosphere is thick enough to prevent the extreme changes between midday heat and midnight cold we will find on Mars.

These reasons made us once think that we could live on Venus without too much trouble. We pictured the planet as a steamy jungle world with great seas and swamps. Some people even thought it might be the way Earth was at the time dinosaurs roamed the world.

Later studies changed that picture. We could find no evidence of either water or oxygen when we studied the reflected light in our spectroscopes. To explain the presence of clouds, science suggested that dust might be the answer. This theory gave a picture of a hot, dry world, barren of life, the surface worn smooth by savage duststorms that swept it, and with an atmosphere of poisonous gas that no man could breathe.

At the present time we cannot even accept that idea. The latest studies have shown that such a guess will not fit all the facts. Scientists today admit that they simply do not know what the atmosphere and clouds of Venus are. Our not being able to find oxygen or water vapor does not prove much, since we cannot see more than the very upper part of the atmosphere. Maybe we could live on Venus; maybe there is some kind of life there much like our own. We do not know.

Before we can explore this world, we must send out a survey ship which can take up an orbit around Venus and make a study of the planet by radar and other means. Only after mapping the surface in this way, and finding more about Venus can we hope to prepare for a trip to the surface.

We can assume that men will land on Venus, and that the trip will be an easier one in many ways than that to Mars. The flight will take less time, and we will not have to stay as long before we can return, so less supplies will be needed. There is no way, however, to give any details on such a trip, until we can find out a great deal more than we now know.

We have now come to the end of the future we can foretell with any accuracy. There are still plenty of worlds to explore, but the effort becomes harder and harder, and we can be less and less sure of what will be found on such trips.

We are in something of the position of Columbus before he sailed from Europe. He knew that the world was round, as a great many men before him had known, in spite of what many others believed. He also knew that India was far away, on what seemed to him was the other side of the world. (He was wrong about the size of Earth, though other men had already figured this out fairly accurately.)

Columbus did not have enough knowledge to chart a safe course. All he knew was that by sailing west he would come to land sooner or later. He had no way of knowing that he would find a whole new continent. Knowledge of America must have existed at the time, but it was buried in old accounts in Scandinavia, where Columbus had no way of learning about the voyage of Leif Ericson.

In the same way, we know a considerable amount about how rockets will work, as Columbus understood his ships. We know some important things about the Universe and the other planets, as he knew about the shape of the Earth. When we try to figure exactly what will happen from what we already know, all we can do is guess. We will probably receive surprises as great as those of Columbus in discovering America. Like him, we may not always know what we have done until long after it has happened.

Still, it would not be fair to stop our story at this point, when we can be reasonably sure men will not stop exploring in space until they have covered the whole Solar

System. There will always be mysteries to be solved and new frontiers to be reached. The rocket will be improved again and again, new fuels will certainly be found, and that which looks extremely difficult at the present time may become fairly easy in the future.

The hottest of all the worlds, Mercury, lies closer to the Sun than Venus. (Once people thought there was another planet even nearer the Sun, named Vulcan, but this belief has long since been disproved.) The pull of the Sun has slowed the rotation of Mercury until it always turns the same face toward the light. There is no air, and the heat on this sunward side is great enough to melt some of the metals, such as lead.

The dark side of Mercury must be bitterly cold—too cold for men to exist for any time, even on exploring expeditions. No light has fallen there for millions of years, and there is no air to carry warmth from the hot side.

Between the extreme heat and the bitter cold, there is a thin strip where men might set up a base. Mercury does not exactly face the Sun the same in every bit of its orbit. Instead, it wobbles a little (this wobbling is known as *libration* to astronomers). As a result, a thin strip of the area of the planet changes from dark to light and back once each 88 days. Ships could land on the planet and the men could explore and study conditions on it, though there could be no hope of finding any life at all like that which we know, since there is no air.

When we go outward beyond Mars, the distance between the planets grows greater and greater, as can be seen in the table on page 88. It does not take much more speed or fuel to reach these distant worlds, but the time spent on the voyages grows greater and greater. A round trip to Jupiter would take 6 years. To reach Pluto, the farthest planet, the time becomes too long for any hope of such a trip until much better rocketships can be built. Even light, which travels 186,000 miles every second, takes more than 5 hours to reach Pluto from the Sun.

The first object beyond Mars is not a true planet, however. Lying between Mars and Jupiter are tiny worlds we have named *asteroids.* There are thousands of these, varying in size from Ceres, which has a diameter of 480 miles, to little bodies of rock too small to be detected at this time. These all move around the Sun in orbits on the same plane as the other planets—known as the *Plane of the Ecliptic.* In spite of some stories, however, these asteroids do not represent any danger to ships. By rising a trifle above this Plane of the Ecliptic, a ship could miss the asteroids completely. While there are a great many of them, they are spread out through such a vast area of space that the chances of coming near one would be pretty faint, unless a ship were looking for them.

It has been suggested that these asteroids may be the remains of another planet beyond Mars which somehow broke up under the pull of Jupiter. Others feel that the material of which the asteroids are composed should have been a planet, but that Jupiter's effects kept it from forming, and that it collected into these small worlds instead. It would be interesting to study the asteroids to find the truth. Their shapes should give us some answer as to how they were created. Also, if they are composed of broken bits of a planet, some of them made up of matter from the heavy planetary core might have interesting deposits of the heavier elements. Whether there could be anything worth mining on them is doubtful, though. Gravity on these small worlds is too low to hold an atmosphere.

Beyond the asteroids lies Jupiter, a huge planet with an immensely deep atmosphere, cold and forbidding. No ship could hope to land on this giant. The pressure of the atmosphere at the surface would be unthinkable, and the effort of fighting away from the pull of gravity here would be hopeless, according to all we know. The same applies to Saturn, lying still farther out, and still colder.

Both of these giant planets, however, have moons that might serve as bases for exploration, and places from which we could study the planets below. Jupiter has four such moons—Io, Europa, Ganymede, and Callisto—which are bigger than our Moon. These moons are airless and extremely cold at this distance from the Sun. We cannot expect to find life on any of them, and even setting up a base would present great difficulties, though it could be done.

Saturn has Titan, a moon almost as large as Mars. This world has an atmosphere, probably of methane. (Such a gas might even be used as a replacement fuel for the rocketship, since this gas burns well.) It would be bitterly cold on Titan, hundreds of degrees below zero, but from it we would be able to study the great, glowing rings that make Saturn the most amazing spectacle in the skies.

These rings are thin bands of material rotating around the giant planet. They lie in such a flat plane that we cannot see them when Saturn is turned to bring them in line with us. At other times, the rings can be seen with any good telescope. These rings are probably made up of countless tiny pieces of rock, all whirling around the planet in orbits like tiny moons, but so numerous that they seem solid when seen from a distance. Like the asteroids, their exact origin is unknown, but they are probably broken pieces of a moon that once circled close to the surface of Saturn.

When we go farther out, we can expect to find even greater cold. Uranus and Neptune are each about 30,000 miles in diameter, less than half that of Jupiter. Their surfaces must be cold enough to freeze most of the gases in our atmosphere. It is likely we could land on either of these worlds and take off again—though it would be almost impossible with the fuels we now have. So far as we can guess, there is not much to interest us on either of these planets.

Finally, at the very edge of the system, we have the little world of Pluto. This planet was not discovered until 1930, and even yet we are unsure about many of the facts about it. It is probably less than 4,000 miles in diameter; we cannot even be certain of its exact size. We can be sure, however, that there is almost no heat on this frigid planet. Almost any gas except hydrogen or helium would have frozen. At such a distance, the Sun is no more than a bright star in the sky. Without a map of the heavens, it could not be located from among the other stars. Even when Pluto is facing the Sun, its surface is in a perpetual gloom, darker than the darkest unclouded night on Earth.

The main item of interest about Pluto is its orbit. The other planets all have orbits that are slightly egg-shaped (elliptical) rather than forming true circles; thus these planets are closer to the Sun at some points than others in those orbits. But the difference from true circles around the Sun is not too great.

In the case of Pluto, however, the orbit varies considerably. At its greatest distance, it is a billion miles farther out than its average distance. At its closest approach to the Sun, it is inside the orbit of Neptune, almost a billion miles less than its average distance out.

This orbit is more like that of a comet than that of a planet, though most comets have even more distorted orbits. This difference has led to much discussion and a number of theories. Some theorists have suggested that Pluto may be a moon of Neptune that was somehow freed to wander off by itself. Its return to the orbit of Neptune would correlate with this idea. Others have wondered whether it is a true member of the Sun's family at all. They suggest that it may have been captured by the Sun from some other star in the distant past, or that it may have wandered out of space and have been caught by the Sun. Perhaps we will never really know the true facts, though exploration of the planet might give us enough information to answer all our questions.

Whether there are other planets even farther out is doubtful. If so, we may never find them. The Sun could hold onto a planet, even at twice the distance of Pluto. Yet finding it in its great orbit would be very difficult. The planet would be dark, since there would be almost no light to be reflected from it, and it would have to be a truly huge world to be found at such a distance. Except to astronomers, who want complete data to use in figuring the behavior of other planets, finding such a tenth planet would be of little use to anyone.

We do know of some bodies that go out into space far beyond the orbit of Pluto, however. These are the *comets.* Many of these travel for billions of miles before they swing about slowly and head back toward the Sun.

Perhaps a comet will be investigated by a spaceship in the future. If so, the investigation will not be done by landing on the comet, almost certainly. From what we can tell, comets are not like the planets. Most of their bulk is made up of gas. This gas is what we see as the tail of a comet. As it approaches the Sun, the gas is thawed from its frozen state. Then the pressure of the light from the Sun (which is real enough to be measured by delicate laboratory instruments) drives this extremely thin gas away from the Sun, and the reflection of light from the gas makes the beacon in the sky which we have seen as the tails of some comets. This also explains why the tail of a comet always points away from the Sun.

The core of the comet is quite small. It

was once thought to be made up of gravel and rocks, but the latest theories indicate it is mostly gas that has not yet thawed, and a few bits of very tiny rock and metal fragments. No matter what the material is, the core of the comet is not large enough to let a ship land properly on it.

On the whole, it does not seem that the Solar System beyond Mars is going to be of much use to us, no matter how good our rockets become. I am afraid that is the truth. We may spend some time on the moons of the outer planets, but we will not stay there. All of these moons will be hard to reach, and none will be hospitable to life. Certainly they offer almost no hope for life to exist on them, or any possibilities of human colonization.

Still, we will have Mars and perhaps Venus to occupy our attention. Only very recently have we been able to learn about the surface of our own world. By the time we are finished with the two nearest planets, our science may have changed so greatly that anything at all can happen. Stories have even been written about moving the outer worlds closer to the Sun. I do not believe this can or will be done, but I would not want to wager too much on it. Nobody can look so far ahead and be sure of anything.

THE SUN'S FAMILY

PLANET	MOONS	MILES DISTANT FROM SUN	DIAMETER IN MILES	ESCAPE VELOCITY MILES A SECOND	SURFACE GRAVITY
Mercury	0	36,002,000	3,100	2.2	.30
Venus	0	67,273,000	7,700	6.3	.86
EARTH	1	93,004,000	7,927	7.0	1.00
Mars	2	141,709,000	4,220	3.1	.38
Jupiter	11	483,881,000	89,000	37.3	2.65
Saturn	9	887,151,000	74,500	22.4	1.18
Uranus	5	1,784,838,000	32,400	13.1	.90
Neptune	2	2,796,693,000	31,000	14.3	1.12
Pluto	0	3,669,699,000	4,000	?	?

CHAPTER 16

colonies in space

We always expect that exploration will be followed by exploitation—that is, the discovery will be followed by the use of whatever is discovered. We have watched such a situation happen again and again in the United States. The first few men went out and found new territory. After them would come a few trappers, hunters and miners. These men would pave the way for the real pioneers, who would come to settle and to colonize. Finally, there would be a well-settled land, where everyone could come to find a safe living.

Maybe use will be made of the planets after they have been explored. If that does happen, such use will have to be different in a number of ways from what it has always been in the past. The pioneer, frontiersman and settler we know from history will not have a chance.

Remember that most of the people who made early use of the new lands were rather poor. They were the ones who could not do what they wanted where they lived, either because of class, religion, lack of money, or for some other reason. The ones who were doing all right stayed where they were. Usually, the settlers moved to the new country because they could not find as much promise at home, not because they wanted adventure. They did not want to fight Indians; they would rather not have had to face danger. The fighting was simply a very unpleasant chore that had to be done so that they might stay alive and get what they wanted. These settlers wanted their children to have more in life than they had, and they *had* to move ahead to get that.

Maybe there will be something on Mars, Venus or the Moon which will offer opportunity to people. We do not know of anything yet, but we cannot say there will not be. If there is, that "something" would have to be very valuable, indeed. In the old days, the miners and trappers who opened up the new lands for later settlers had furs and metals to send back to civilization for the things they needed. The furs and metals were items they could carry on their backs, on horseback or in wagons.

Anything worth sending back to Earth by rocketship will have to be extremely valuable. We cannot even guess at the cost of carrying freight in such a way, except that the rates will be extremely high. We know, however, that several hundred pounds of fuel are needed to ship 1 pound of freight from Earth to the station and then from the station to the Moon. If we can lower that amount until it only takes 100 pounds of fuel for 1 of freight—which would be very good indeed—and we can cheapen our fuel to only 5 cents a pound, the cost will still be 5 dollars per pound. All the other costs must be added on, too.

That cost does not seem exorbitant, but we have only covered half the trouble. Remember that it will require a great many pounds of cargo to supply a man with all the food and other things he will need for a year on the Moon. Whatever is found on the Moon will have to pay for its own freight, all the freight of the man's supplies, and enough profit to make him choose the hard life on the Moon to the easier one on Earth. If he has a family, the amount of essential supplies will be much greater, and he will have to find something even more valuable to pay for them. Pure gold that he could dig out with a shovel might not be worth the trouble.

There is another drawback. Before he can go, he must have enough money to pay for the trip and the supplies he will need. This will require quite a few thousand dollars to reach the Moon, and tens of thousands to reach another planet, even allowing for much lower costs than those which would prevail if we were making such trips right now. If a man has that much money, he can probably invest it in a business on Earth that will take care of all his needs. He will not feel the necessity of going to the Moon!

If the man has the money and still wants to go, it still will not be a simple matter. There will not be many rocketships, and besides these will be much too expensive for a person to build or to have built. The Government and a few big corporations will be the only ones who will own such ships. They will want to use them for their own purposes. Anyone who wants to make such a trip will have to be valuable to either the Government or a business.

Only men in the very best physical condition will be accepted, and they also will be expected to have had a very high level of education in some science or skill that will be of use on the other worlds. The requirements will be so stiff that only the very finest men will be able to pass the tests. (A man who can pass such a test and has the money to pay his way would have no need to leave Earth, naturally.)

Very few men will qualify for space travel or for settling on other planets. We cannot expect a rapid spread of men through space like the rush to settle the Old West in the United States. There will be only a few who will be sent to the other planets and the Moon, and colonies must develop from the small exploring teams.

Science will want to study the other worlds fully, and such study can only be made by years of work and teams of men. Once the first exploration has opened up a world, other people will be sent to continue the exploration. To defray the cost, a great deal of money will be needed, but the money will be found, because we know by this time that every bit of knowledge we gain somehow pays for itself. It is good business to spend money on science. (At one time, astronomy seemed to have no practical use. Who cared about finding out what happened in stars that were thousands of billions of miles away? Yet it was this work in astronomy that provided the knowledge that led in time to atomic power and the hydrogen bomb.)

Some men and women will go out into space to stay for years, since it will be cheaper than it would be to transport them back and forth, and also because there will be some studies that will take them years to finish. Naturally, not all will be scientists; for a full-scale exploration, there will be a need for cooks, mechanics and numerous other occupations. Also, since it will be cheaper, everything that can be found or made on the new world will be used.

We have already shown that this possibility may mean digging into the surface of the Moon, mining rock that will supply water and air, and growing plants in hydroponic tanks. Because of the power that can be obtained from the sunlight, much can be done to make the Moon self-supporting.

On Mars, many details are similar to conditions on Earth, and the job of living off that planet may be somewhat easier. Here the settlers will probably begin with airtight buildings made of some kind of plastic—perhaps even supported by inflated sections, just as small swimming pools are now being made to be inflated. Such houses have already been suggested for use on Earth.

In time, it may prove simpler to put a big, transparent plastic dome over the whole group of houses in order to hold in breathable air. The oxygen the people will need may already be in the atmosphere, even though we can find no sign of it. In that case, maybe it could be compressed for breathing. Otherwise, the oxygen could be separated from water, as on the Moon. There is very little water on Mars, but a certain amount freezes each winter to form the cap around each pole. This could be collected and used.

Growing the food would not be too difficult. There is a good prospect that our plants could be grown in Martian soil, provided hothouses are covered with more of the transparent plastic to protect the plants from the extreme temperature changes on Mars.

Settlers on the planet would thus obtain their own food, air, water and clothing from plant fibers. Perhaps they could even find enough metal ores for most of the tools and machines they would need. Power would probably have to come from one of the smaller atomic generating plants that are already being designed. With all this development, men would be able to live off the planet, except for a very few supplies the ships would have to bring them from Earth.

It would be possible to keep a group of several hundred men based on Mars, some of whom might stay there for several years or more. The group would include both men and women; many of these would marry and have families there.

It is from these children and their children that colonies might grow up in time. In all previous colonizations of new territory, naturally most of the first population has moved in from the outside. Transportation to space is far too expensive and difficult for that, so the colonies may grow up on Mars, the Moon, and even Venus (which may be easier to settle than Mars, though we cannot tell) from a very few original people. If every family averages 3 children, the second generation will be 50 percent greater than the first. That method seems a slow way for a colony to grow, but such a group might increase in that manner from 300 at the start to a million after 600 years. If the number of children in each family were more than 3, the time of growth would be much less.

These settlements can grow, if there is a way for people to live on other planets, either without supplies from Earth, or by the settlers being able to provide something to trade to Earth which will justify the high freight cost. If the colony is to increase in population, though, the children there will have to remain on the planet from the very beginning, instead of deciding to return to Earth as they grow up.

We can guess why they might stay on other planets. On the lighter worlds, they would grow up adapted to less gravity, and they might not even be able to stand the return trip to Earth, or to live comfortably on our world if they did come back. Also, at first there will be plenty to keep children busy as they grow up, studying the world around them. For several generations, at least, we shall be happy to have more people growing up there, where they can increase the size of the group without having to be carried there by rocket—and where they will grow up better able to adjust themselves to the new world than would someone from Earth.

To the children growing up there, Mars—or the Moon, or Venus—will seem more like home than Earth. Because of the children, the parents will probably try even harder to make the world livable for them.

You can be sure that when they first arrive on a new world, both parents and children will keep talking about when they will go back to Earth. That is just human nature. When immigrants came over to the United States from Europe, many talked about their homelands. Most of them became adjusted and stayed, however. Some people surely will come back to Earth from the planets. Others will keep putting the trip off, until they do a little more work. By then their children will feel less need to return to Earth. After a few generations, they would give up the idea, and begin to consider themselves Martians.

Suppose the settlers find nothing on the planets that they can sell to Earth because of the high freight rates?

In that case, people may have to be brought back to Earth someday, but even then they may find a way to stay on the new worlds. Grants for scientific research and the Government will pay the expenses for quite a while. By the time payment begins to stop, the colonists should have made much progress toward finding a way to live on their worlds. They will have to give up many of the comforts we know, and they will have hardships we do not like. But the early settlers of the United States left all comforts behind them and were faced with great difficulties, too, when they arrived.

In the situation of people already on Mars, for instance, the high cost of going there has no meaning. To those, the cost keeps them from going back to Earth. They are already on Mars, where it is much cheaper to develop what they can find than to try to make enough money for the long, expensive return. In addition, they will have their specialized work on Mars, and they will not even be sure of making a way for themselves on our world.

There will be new trades, perhaps—not carpenters as we know them, but men trained to work with what can be found on Mars. There will be many such trades, because no group of hundreds of people can live with only scientists and technicians among them. Someone has to make clothes, cook the food, farm the plants, handle the machines, and perform all the other tasks necessary for survival.

Once the people have more experience at finding and using the resources Mars can provide, and once there are more than a few hundred people there, I believe that we will have colonies growing up, never to return to Earth.

There will be few trips between planets then, probably, but the inhabitants will not be out of touch with Earth. Radio waves can cover the distance to Mars very easily. It does not take any great amount of power, either, if we use frequencies like those in radar. Stations equipped with much smaller than our usual broadcasting transmitters can carry on easy conversations with Mars, once the settlers get there.

It will be good, in the long run, to have such colonies. The new things the colonists learn will be reported back to Earth, to make our lives better. Meantime, what is learned on this world will help the settlers

in fitting the planets to their lives. The differences between the worlds will lead to inventions and discoveries that will be good for all the planets.

Of course, the colonists may find something that will be valuable enough to pay the cost of sending freight back and forth.

When people today ask what good will result from getting to the planets, they usually mean something in terms of money. We can answer about the value of the space station, but we cannot honestly say that anything on the other worlds will pay anyone a single cent.

However, if Columbus had known what he would find at the end of his voyage, he would not have sailed—and Queen Isabella would not have given him money for the ships he needed. Columbus was looking for a route to the riches of India. Instead, he found the New World, filled with savages, and with no sign of the spices he wanted. He made three trips, hoping to find India, and he failed.

It was not until later that men discovered enough about the New World to make it pay. Then it turned out to be worth infinitely more than any route to India could ever have been. There was gold in the New World, but the real wealth lay in new commodities, some of which had never been used before. Today, corn and potatoes are basic foods for a great deal of the world, and they came from America. Our first medicine that could really cure a disease came from the New World—the bark of a South American tree which could cure the terrible disease of malaria. Nobody can place any value on the lives that the drug, quinine, has saved.

By the time the small colonies have used up the funds allotted for scientific investigation of the planets, there seems a good chance that the inhabitants will find something valuable enough to make living on those worlds profitable.

There will be no covered wagons and gold rushes in space, but the colonies will grow without them. Someday, men will look up into the night sky with the warm feeling that there are friends and neighbors up there!

SECTION V

the far future

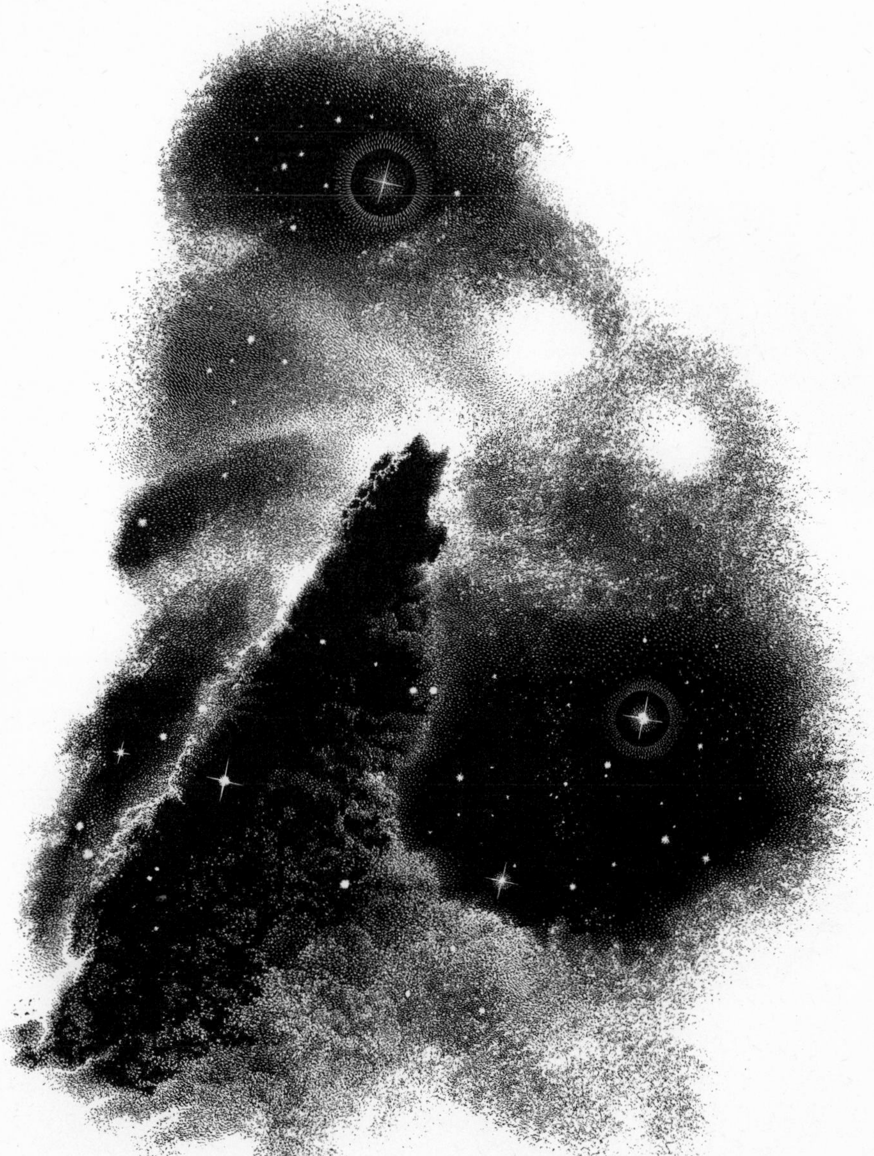

CHAPTER 17

stuff and nonsense

SPACE is so vast that we can find no end to it. If a man could start out at a million miles an hour and go on for a million years, he would only cover a very small section of the Universe our telescopes show us.

Yet man has proved to be a quite remarkable creature, one who can learn to do easily what his ancestors thought could never be done. Two hundred years ago, a man could travel little over 20 miles in a day. A hundred years before our time, a distance of 200 miles was a long day's travel. Today we can fly 3,000 miles between breakfast and dinner. Within a few more years, we can probably reach a million miles in one day, on journeys between the planets.

Some writers have given us stories of flights between the stars that would take less time than a trip to the next town does now. They think of men spreading out through all the Universe, to the very end of space. In a few stories, they have even written about men finding the end of space (if we can try to imagine that!) and breaking out beyond it.

This type of conjecture is only wild fantasy. I cannot say that even the wildest idea is completely improbable, but neither can I write about such things as if we will do them. In fact, at this writing we have covered almost all that I can honestly feel sure will happen.

Once we have reached the planets, and perhaps set up colonies, present science has come to the end of what it can predict. I do not think we have run out of enough "future," but we have run out of enough sure knowledge to predict anything accurately. From now on, we have to guess about what more can be done. We have a few facts, and we have some ideas about the Universe, but we cannot describe what will be done, as we could when we described the trip to the Moon.

It would not be fair to stop without speculating about what the future beyond our present knowledge may bring, just as people wondered about flying machines before anyone really believed in such things. We will have to remember that this whole section is to be considered the "far future," too far away for us to forsee clearly.

However, there are a few things that we can be sure will *not* happen. It is much easier to find out about those than it is to predict what can happen—just as we can be reasonably certain that airplanes cannot fly to the Moon. Even before men had any idea of how we could reach the satellite of Earth, they knew ways in which we could not reach it!

Before we speculate about what might happen, then, let us first get rid of some of the impossible or highly unlikely ideas.

One of these ideas is the picture of having the planets war with each other, sending out great fleets of spaceships against each other. This almost certainly will not happen. Even if two planets as close as Earth and Venus tried to start an interplanetary war without thought of cost or effort, they could not wage it with any degree of success.

In space, ships must move at great speeds. They travel at anywhere from 50,000 to 100,000 miles an hour! They have to build up such speeds to be able to make the trips; if they tried to go more slowly, the tremendous pull of solar gravity would drag them toward the Sun.

Now, if two ships—or fleets of ships—going at such speeds were to meet, they would be many miles apart in one second after coming together! Before they could aim and fire their weapons, the enemy would be beyond range. They would have only that one opportunity, too; it would take time to slow down and reverse their speeds in order to meet again.

To make matters harder, ships heading from Venus to Earth would not be on the same orbit as those heading from Earth to Venus. Their chance of meeting each other in space would be very small.

No rocketship conceivable (even with atomic fuel that worked perfectly) could hope to carry enough fuel to lift the huge load of armor and weapons and still be able to start and stop in space often enough to be useful as a warship. Nor could the ship be used to attack a planet. On Earth, for instance, radar warning could tell us of the approach of any ship big enough to cause much damage. Then small, automatic rockets from Earth or from the station could knock the enemy ship out of the sky before any damage could be done. It is always going to be much easier to build such missiles than man-carrying rockets, since they need no return fuel, no living space, and no long trip to reach the target. For use against another planet, they would be useless, because control signals would take too long to reach them in space, but they would work perfectly near our home world.

Against a planet, any spaceship will be a tiny, weak weapon. It would be ridiculous for one planet to attempt to conquer another world.

Except for conquest, even to think of space war would be ridiculous. It would serve no purpose. If Venus, for example, wanted freedom from Earth, she could have it without war. She could simply refuse all Earth ships the right to land. They could not hope to get through the missiles she could send up, so they would have to stay away. We could not drop enough troops from spaceships to matter, either. A planet can have millions of people living on it, but a spaceship would be overcrowded with a thousand! A few thousand troops would have no chance against the weapons of a whole world.

Space war would be so expensive that no one can even think of what it would cost, and it would accomplish nothing at all. No planet or ruler would ever be able to start such a war, and none would ever think about it seriously.

Of course, there are those mysterious "ray guns" and weapons! They are, however, more of the ideas that should be called fantasy, not science. We have studied every kind of radiation, from the long radio waves to the ultra-short cosmic rays, and no such mysterious "rays" exist as are found in some fiction. There are not even gaps in the range of radiation into which we can fit them.

If some new discovery were made by which something similar to these rays could be found, they still would not change conditions. They would be no better for war in space than cannons and atomic bombs. We can build cannon that will reach farther than we can see to aim—and in space we could shoot a great deal farther. Rays would require just as accurate an aim to work, and would be no better than the cannon. In fact, it is difficult to think of anything that could cause more damage to a spaceship than a small cannonball hitting it. At its speed, and with the speed of the ship which fired it, a single small cannon shell would blow up a whole spaceship. Likewise, a revolver would be the most horrible weapon that could be used against a man in a spacesuit. One hole anywhere in the suit would rob him of his air and probably kill him!

The weapons we have would be so much more effective in space than they are on Earth that it would be only a waste to try to improve them!

Piracy in space is almost as certainly not going to amount to much. A pirate would have to have a ship that was stronger and more dangerous than the usual rocket. Such a ship would be so expensive that it would not pay to build one. If a pirate had enough money to buy such a ship—probably none would be for sale, anyway—he would be so rich that he would not bother to turn pirate.

Even if he did turn pirate because he was completely insane and could find an insane crew to go with him, it would do him no good. He might even somehow steal a ship, but the fuel for it would be down on the planets, where a spaceship is a poor, weak thing compared to any weapons the planets might have. A pirate could not get fuel to keep going.

Nor could the pirate sell the material he pirated. Most of it would be worthless—just supplies for the colonies—and the rest would be so valuable that careful records would be kept of everything. When he tried to find a buyer, he would learn that only the Government handled the material, and the Government would not pay him for what he had stolen! He would end up somewhere without fuel for his ship, regretting that he had ever thought about piracy!

Space is going to be quite peaceful. There might be crime or even war on any one of the planets, but such a situation simply is not worth bothering with out in space. There will not be enemy warships lurking around the next asteroid, nor pirates with their hideouts on some world where the space patrol cannot catch them. There will not even be a space patrol, because it will not be necessary. Those ideas are all fine for stories that are only meant to be fun, but such things will not happen in any future we can foresee.

We will not even find hordes of enemy aliens out in space, almost certainly. None of the planets except Venus would have any chance for a form of life which could have developed so complex a mechanical civilization as on Earth. We can almost assume that Venus does not, either. If she did have intelligent life, her machinery would be giving off radio interference, and she would be using some form of radio for communications, probably. We could detect the radio, and we do not find anything of that nature.

It would be hard for inhabitants of Venus to get into space, anyhow. The planet has no moon for the first step, and she does not have a space station, since we would undoubtedly be able to spot that as it circled over the clouds. Without something like a space station from which to start space travel, getting rockets to other planets would be more trouble than the first work done on it would be worth.

We are getting radio signals from Jupiter at the present time. We have been picking them up for some time, but here we can say what they are not, even though we cannot say exactly what causes them. We know enough about the basic facts of signaling to tell if the signals contain any intelligence or information, even if we could not understand any of it. The Jupiter signals are not real signals at all; they are simply the result of some natural phenomenon on Jupiter.

Some people, however, feel sure that the aliens from outer space have found us already. By this they mean the "flying saucers," about which so much fuss has been made. People seem to feel that anything science cannot explain perfectly and which is seen in the sky is a ship of little green men from Venus or the stars, that has come down here to study us. They also seem to think that the United States Army and the scientists are in some kind of conspiracy to hide the truth, since neither group will admit that there are flying saucers. Actually, while a few scientists might deny anything unfamiliar, most men of science spend their lives trying to find new things. Almost any military expert, engineer or scientist would give 10 years off his life for a real opportunity to get a good look at a true alien spaceship!

I wish there were ships from space; it would make me feel much happier about our being able to build ships that could travel easily and cheaply between the stars. So far, all the proof I have found has been much less than I would need to believe in the discovery of a new kind of grasshopper.

I have looked at pictures that show nothing but some kind of vague, uncertain blotches. I know that a good camera can take sharp pictures of anything the size and distance reported for the saucer; enlargement should show many details. When these pictures are enlarged, they still show nothing. (One book on the subject does contain very clear pictures. However, the flying saucer shown is nothing but the reflector from an old-style lamp—like the one I played with as a child. Anybody who knows anything about metal construction could see it was a small object, made to look large by a closeup photograph! That illustration was in an account by someone who had claimed to have been in such a ship!)

I have read such accounts, and have found strange statements that could not be true of anything that flies so fast through the air. When these errors are mentioned, this supposedly complete account is suddenly changed so that the error is no longer there! I have studied books explaining the saucers, and the writers have made mistakes in elementary science that are proof they cannot report on things we do know, much less be trusted about things from outer space.

So far, I have found no real proof of flying saucers. To a real saucer fan, lack of proof means nothing. He has a standard reply: "Why can't there be saucers? You can't prove there aren't, can you?"

Of course, I cannot—nobody can. Nobody can prove that these are not bubbles built by fairies, either. Nobody could possibly believe all the things we cannot prove wrong. Science does not operate that way. In his work, a scientist has to believe only what he *can* prove. If you can show real proof of flying saucers—something that cannot be explained *better* without such a complicated idea as this—you will be believed by scientists. The proof, though, is the responsibility of the person who says they do exist. It is not anyone else's job to prove that the saucer fan is wrong.

Yet scientists have studied the information on the saucers. One man, Dr. Donald H. Menzel of Harvard University, made a thorough study of them. He found that the stories were not new at all; 50 and 100 years ago, people were seeing the same things, just as he had seen one which started him investigating. He put all the accounts together and then looked for the simplest explanation. It proved very simple.

Some of these phenomena were mistaken observations of weather balloons and other objects. (I know of a group of people who reported seeing a saucer. At dusk, they saw a toy balloon being carried above the trees by the wind. It looked far away, and its little jerky motions looked like huge jumps. Unfortunately for the story, I heard it from the man who climbed up and got the balloon, after the newspaper had been called. The paper printed it as a flying-saucer sighting.)

But most people had seen something unusual in the air. Menzel discovered that layers of hot and cold air can behave like a lens, to throw light back toward the ground. Something miles away, or the headlights of distant cars, can be bent (*refracted*) in this way, so that we see saucers right over our heads. The motions of the air currents also can make what we see appear to move and turn at amazing speeds. Even radar can be fooled in much the same way. Menzel even built a small model of this action in his laboratory, to show exactly how it works.

This does not prove that somewhere there may not be a real space traveler in some kind of ship. It does give us a simple, believable explanation that fits the facts much better than most of the complicated, poorly explained accounts of ships from outer space. Usually when a simple explanation fits the facts, it is much better than any amount of unproved fancy theories.

Besides, if space travel has been going on over our heads for 50 years already without the alien race bothering us, we do not have much to worry about. Either that race is too stupid to communicate with one of our scientists and reveal itself, or else the aliens just do not care about us one way or the other.

There does not seem to be much expectation that we will encounter any alien races in space around our Sun. Without other beings, without wars and piracy, outer space is going to be very tame for some people. There is enough real difficulty and danger to space travel as things are, though, and that will have to do. With all of space as a challenge, we have no need to invent problems that will probably never happen.

CHAPTER 18

atomic power or sails?

WHENEVER we begin to talk about what we can do in the future of space travel, one huge problem arises: we must have better fuels for our rockets than those we use now.

True, we can reach Mars and Venus with hydrazine hydrate and nitric acid. At a great deal of expense, we can send ships back and forth while these worlds are being explored and colonized, but with our present fuels, we cannot afford to make many trips, and we cannot carry any great amount of freight on any one trip.

If we want to go to the other planets, getting there becomes more difficult. We could send a ship to the moons of Jupiter, but it would take six years. The farther out into space we go, the more difficult space travel becomes. Only a little more speed is needed for a trip to Pluto than for one to Mars, and our fuel could do the job—but nobody would want to make such a lifelong trip. Even if people were willing, the quantity of food and supplies needed would make it impossible.

On the other hand, if we could find greatly improved fuels, many of these obstacles would be eliminated. Such fuels would have to be easily stored and used, since we would not gain much by having to increase the size of the tanks and add almost as much weight to the ship as the new fuel would save. Thus while liquid hydrogen and liquid oxygen together have a much higher exhaust velocity than the fuels we now use, they are too hard to handle. The new fuels must be liquid at normal temperatures. They must be *stable*—that is, they must not break down or explode by themselves. They must be cheap enough to produce so that they can be used practically. They must serve to cool the rocket tube as well as to power it, to prevent the tube from burning out.

It would be convenient, too, if we could have both our fuel and our oxidizer together in one liquid. There is one such *monopropellant,* nitromethane, which does everything by itself and is a liquid that is not too hard to control. So far, nobody can trust it not to explode when it is not supposed to, instead of it doing so just inside the rocket. If we could find a single fuel to work properly, it would greatly reduce the bulk of our tanks and the difficulty of handling it.

The most important improvement, however, will be in the speed, or velocity, of the exhaust. If we could double the exhaust velocity, we would do more than double the effective work the fuel could do. As we saw in Chapter 3, doubling the exhaust velocity will permit us to get almost three times as much speed out of the same amount of fuel

—or achieve the same speed with much less fuel.

If we could obtain four times as much velocity out of our exhaust, results would be even better. Then we could expect the same amount of fuel to give our ship a final speed *twenty times as great* as that of our present fuel! This would be enough improvement to make trips to all the planets feasible. The improved fuel would allow us to run regular ferry trips to the Moon, and would make practical a regular and fairly frequent cargo-carrying service to Mars and back. In fact, if a fuel is developed with four times as much exhaust velocity as the one we have now, most of our wildest dreams could come true. We could even save immense amounts of money by using a two-stage rocket instead of the huge three-stage one to reach the space station! With such a fuel, we would not have to take the most economical orbit to the planets, but could cut across from one planet to the other somewhat, shortening the trip tremendously.

However, we do not know of any fuel that would give us that great an exhaust velocity. The very best theoretical fuel offers only a trifle more than twice the exhaust velocity of our present mixture. Even to double the figure would be a big step forward, but it would not be quite enough for all we would like to do.

We will undoubtedly find better fuels, such as ones that use fluorine instead of oxygen. Even a slight improvement is going to make everything much easier for us and speed our conquest of the planets. To get the fuels we really need, on the other hand, we will have to do better than it now seems we can possibly do.

This does not mean we cannot ever develop such fuels. There was a time when uranium was the heaviest element we could ever hope to find, but now men have made several heavier elements by using tricks that were not even thought of a few years ago. Perhaps the chemists and physicists will find some new principle of science which will let them make fuels much better than any we can even dream of today, but we do not know how it can be done, and we cannot count on it.

How about atomic fuels, then? This suggestion has been made time and again, since the atom now seems to be the answer to everything in the future.

Well, we almost certainly will not have atomic *fuel,* though we just might develop a way to make atomic power work. We already know just about every individual type of atom, and there is no kind of atom or combination of atoms that will act as atomic fuel. The rocket gets its power from a chemical explosion, and it would not help for the fuel to be radioactive as an atomic fuel would be.

However, the breakdown of the atom can give us enormous power. Even a small amount of radioactive matter can provide a tremendous flow of energy. That, of course, is what we need for our spaceship, but harnessing the energy is a tough problem.

In the first place, while the fuel required by the atomic pile is not very heavy, the pile itself is very ponderous. It takes tons of other material to make the pile work safely. There must be shielding for the men who will ride in the ships, and material which will moderate the activity—that is, regulate it so it works properly. So far, every atomic power plant that will give large amounts of energy is an extremely heavy mass, and we have no idea of a way to shield it without adding excessively to the weight. (Maybe it can be done someday, but we cannot see any method at this time.)

Then we must remember that our rocket has to deliver a fantastic amount of power for a short period. Tons of fuel are burned every second for the first few minutes, and then the ship coasts. We might cut down some of that early power and keep going on acceleration for a longer time, but we still would have to consume far more energy during the takeoff than we need for almost anything else.

This means that the atomic pile would have to deliver all that energy—and would have to be big enough to handle it. We have not built piles that large yet. The one used in the atomic submarine is much lower in power than the one we would need.

Finally, we have to find some way of changing the energy of the pile from heat to a drive for the ship. This is not easy to do. At present, we have to move the heat out of the pile by piping liquids through it. These liquids then heat water (or another liquid) in what is called a heat exchanger, and the steam produced runs a steam turbine, which then runs a generator to produce electricity. All this equipment is heavy, and there is a considerable loss of energy at every step—a factor difficult to cope with on a spaceship, where the lost energy would appear as waste heat that would be almost impossible to remove.

We have to change the heat of atomic power into electricity, however, since we have no way to harness the heat directly. An atomic pile cannot run at a high enough temperature to produce a steam jet with enough exhaust to drive a rocket successfully. The pile would begin going to pieces at such a high temperature.

We do not know exactly how to use this electricity yet, either, but at least we have some ideas that may work out in time. Our problem is to drive something backward at a high speed, in order to move the ship forward. We still have to produce a fuel which will furnish an exhaust.

We already know how to break down molecules into what are known as ions—atoms which have an electric charge on them. We do this every time we plate a piece of metal or light a fluorescent bulb, so it is not too difficult to do. We also know how to make such electrically charged particles move at a high speed by surrounding them with coils of wire in which an electric current flows. Many of the big atom-smashing machines work this way, and they can drive the particles to very high speeds.

We cannot do it practically yet, but it seems that sometime in the future we may find ways of getting such an "ionic" or "electronic" drive, powered by some development of atomic energy. You can be almost sure that men will have reached the planets before these new types of drives are developed, however.

Such drives might give us really incredible exhaust velocities. Our present fuels can yield speeds of only 2 or 3 miles a second of exhaust, but such "ionic" drives might give exhaust speeds as high as 100 or even 100,000 miles a second! The particles in the atom-smashing machines that use something of the same idea already are speeded up to many thousands of miles a second. In that case, only a small amount of fuel would have to be blasted away to drive the ships to very high speeds. Trips might be made in a much shorter time than we have considered, and payloads might be carried at a much lower rate, making true colonies much more practical. Such ships would still need heavy atomic plants, and would be very expensive, but they might prove much cheaper in the end.

In fiction, there have been suggestions for various other ways to move a ship, without needing any rocket or rocket exhaust. These descriptions of "space warp," "inertialess drive," and "paragravity" actually do not mean anything. They are just words the writer has used to make it seem his ships can do more than rockets. The terms sound scientific, but they are no more workable than would be suggestions about driving the ships by black magic!

Maybe in the very far future, some way to move through space without rockets will be found, but we have no idea at all of how that will be done, or whether it is possible. With one exception, which I will describe shortly, we know of no method of traveling in space without using something like a rocket.

Even the old idea of "cutting off gravity" will not help us. We know what gravity does, but we do not really know anything else about it. We do not know whether it can be "cut off." If we could find something that would stop gravity, we still could not get something for nothing. There is a law of physics, known as the *conservation of energy,* which states that the amount of energy going in and that coming out of any operation must be the same. (Work—such as lifting weights—can only be performed by using energy.) To lift any object into space takes energy. It does not matter what method you use, the energy must still be supplied. In the case of a shield that cuts off gravity, this energy must be supplied to move the object onto the shield; to lift it out of our gravity onto the shield will then require as much energy as that needed to drive it beyond Earth's gravity by any other means.

Like most devices other than rockets, the *gravity shield* offers no practical hope of letting us move through space. Yet there is one way to operate a ship between the worlds without using rockets. The idea may seem ridiculous at first, when we remember there is no air—and hence no wind—between the planets. Strangely enough, the trick is at least theoretically workable.

A ship can be moved in space by using sails!

For a ship of this sort, the energy needed would be provided by the pressure of light. We have already read that this pressure is enough to force the tail of a comet away from the Sun. Scientists have also seen clouds of gas hurled up from the Sun's surface by such pressure. It is also possible to measure this light pressure on delicate laboratory instruments. Small as this pressure is, it still provides a real source of energy.

The above idea has been suggested several times. In an article by Russell Saunders in *Astounding Science Fiction* enough details were worked out to show that a ship using sails actually could be built. The sail would have to be of very thin metal, and it would be several miles in diameter, but it could be assembled.

Such sailing ships of space would have to stay several thousand miles beyond the planets, where the pull of gravity would not be too great, and they would be useful only in moving freight from planet to planet. Rockets would have to be used to ferry the supplies up to the ships from the planets. The ships would move much more slowly than rockets, but would have the advantage of being able to keep moving steadily, rather than slowing steadily, as the rocket must.

The ships would move most easily in a direction away from the Sun, of course. To turn back, they would need some planet around which they could swing, using the gravity to change their course. They could navigate to some extent, just as a sailing ship does, by using the sail at an angle. Sunlight striking at an angle to the sail and bouncing off would create some side thrust which they could use.

Just how useful these ships would be is rather doubtful. They would be slow, and the supplies for the crews might require so much space that they would have no advantage over regular rockets. The sails would be delicate apparatus, as well as being so huge that they might be very difficult to handle.

Probably no such ships will ever be built, unless very small ones are tried at some time for sporting events, or simply to test out how they might work. In spite of the huge quantities of fuel a rocket uses—against no need for fuel on these ships—the practical advantages are all with the rocket.

Still, it is an interesting idea to consider. Imagine what life might be like on a ship sailing from world to world!

It is also rather curious to know that the only method of travel that might compete with a rocket is the oldest idea of all. Men were using sails before the wheel was invented, and such sails probably were the first great mechanical invention. Now it seems that the idea is still good for more thought, even in competition with one of our latest inventions.

Or is the rocket such a new invention, after all? It is nothing but the work of two gases, burning together in a carefully shaped tube. It employs a more direct use of a special form of fire than most other machines we have—and fire, of course, is the oldest of all man's discoveries.

However, it is not how new or old an idea is that matters; it is how well we can make it work. In the case of the rocket, whether atomic-powered or driven by new and improved chemical fuels, we can be quite sure that new ways will be found to better its operation. Whether we can ever find ways good enough to take us beyond the planets out to the stars, is a question we cannot answer. We can only hope.

CHAPTER 19

other eyes watching

ONE of the dreams in many minds for a long time is that of finding other intelligent life on the outer worlds. Hundreds of years ago, men were writing of trips to other worlds, where strange but intelligent beings were found.

This hope rose to a fever pitch when Schiaparelli announced the "canals" of Mars. The misunderstanding about the meaning of the word made people think of trenches dug by civilized creatures, instead of their being some kind of natural channels. Great plans were made to signal the Martians. Some people wanted to have sections of our forests burned in patterns that would form huge letters; others wanted us to build great mirrors in our deserts; still others wanted us to dig huge canals of our own.

Later, after radio was discovered, the hope of intelligent life on Mars rose again. This time we were to erect big transmitters and beam signals to the Martians, while others searched the ether to find the signals they were sure the Martians must be sending us.

Lately, the flying-saucer stories have started the hope all over again. Many people believe in the saucers, because they hope that there are other forms of life which will get in touch with us. Others, like myself, cannot believe that saucers come from space, but we do wish there could be truth in the stories. It would be nice to meet another type of intelligent life.

There is good reason attached to this hope, too. If some other race has developed civilization, it seems plausible that what those people have learned in some fields of endeavor will be greater than our knowledge—just as we probably will have discovered things they have not. Such ideas could be exchanged to the profit of both races. Even without any increase in scientific information, we could learn a great deal more about ourselves and about all life if we had another race to study.

There are stories of alien enemies coming from the stars, but we are not too worried about those. A race advanced enough to build spaceships and visit us should be too intelligent to start a war that could do nobody any good. If we develop space travel first and visit the so-called aliens, we shall be too interested in learning all about them to think of fighting, and we can be almost positive they will feel the same way.

Sadly, it now appears that we have very little chance of finding such intelligent life on the planets of our own Sun. Maybe there is life on Venus, but we do not know about it, and we cannot hope for it until we visit the planet. We have to assume that we are the only intelligent race in the Solar System, not because we are egotistic about our own importance, but simply because the indications are that it is true. The other planets simply are not well-designed for any kind of life that would develop intelligence.

Does this mean there can be no intelligent life besides ours in the Universe? At one time science thought so, but this is no longer the best answer.

Fifteen or twenty years ago, it seemed that our Sun might be the only one (or one of very, very few) that had planets around it in the whole Universe. Every theory of how the planets were formed had faults; as the astronomers tried to fill the gaps in their explanations, the chances of such an event as the birth of planets from a sun grew rarer and rarer. They were talking about very tricky collisions of very rare types of stars to pull planets out of one of those stars.

Then more careful study showed that even the trickiest collision would not explain some of the facts. The planets had too much angular momentum—that is, momentum in the form of motion around the Sun—for any of the former ideas to be correct. The whole idea of a collision between stars had to be abandoned, which left the astronomers with no explanation at all. They could not say whether our Sun was the only star with planets, or whether every star had a family around it.

About that time, evidence appeared to show that at least two other stars did have planets. These would have to be very large planets, larger even than Jupiter. Otherwise, we could not have detected them at such great distances. If big planets could exist outside our system, probably others could also, and that would mean many suns might have planets.

Since then, new theories about how planets are formed have been worked out. These ideas are rather complicated, but a general explanation can be given.

There are sections of space where great clouds of gas exist. It seems probable that our Sun was formed from such a cloud, and that it began to clump together at the center, under the pull of gravity. As the Sun formed, the pull of gravity grew stronger, pulling in more of the gas, increasing the pull, etc. This set up a swirling motion in space, much like a whirlpool, or the swirling water being drawn down the bathtub drain. At the center of this whirlpool, the pressure built up steadily until it reached a point where it was packing the atoms more and more tightly, until they began to start atomic reactions. The heat of those reactions gave us the star we call our Sun.

While the center was collecting, other things were happening. The gas swirling in from outside was now being hurled back by the radiation from the central Sun. It no longer swirled inward smoothly, but it was still circling. (You might see something like this if a valve could be turned so that water was suddenly coming up through the drain while the water in the tub was still turning from its momentum.) Little local whirlpools were set up around the center, and the gas began collecting at the center of each of these. These were smaller near the center, but farther out they were quite large. Out of these whirlpools—still moving in their circular paths—the planets were formed, with the smaller planets inward and the larger ones beyond. Other little eddies and irregularities gave us moons.

The mathematics behind this theory are rather complicated, and the picture is not quite that direct and simple. However, this is the basic idea that seems to give the best explanation of how our Solar System was formed. It makes the formation of the planets part of the same process by which the Sun was formed, and it explains a great deal that the older ideas did not even try to cover.

The nice thing about this interpretation is that it probably applies to the formation of most suns. According to this theory, almost all of the stars had a good opportunity to develop planets. In some systems of many suns close together or circling each other, the planets may have had no room to exist, but there will still be a great many stars with planets—millions and millions of them in space. The chances are excellent that stars similar to our Sun will have systems of planets much like our own.

Out of all these millions of planetary systems, there must be several worlds not too different from Earth.

Will such worlds have life something like our own on them? Science cannot say positively, but the expectations are very good for such life.

We cannot expect to see living beings that look like us, but we can feel fairly safe in believing that among all the stars there must be many that have planets that are the homes of intelligent beings. Even if most of the worlds are farther behind us in developments or have life that has gone in different directions, there is a good possibility that these planets will contain beings that are civilized and intelligent. We can guess that there may be worlds where the intelligent life is still living in caves and chipping whatever they use for flint, while other worlds may already have rocketships moving among their planets. Such an idea is not too ridiculous.

These inhabited planets, however, may lie at great distances from each other. The nearest star to us is still so far away that light from it takes more than 4 years to reach us—that is why astronomers say it is more than 4 light-years away. Since light travels about 6 million million miles a year (6 trillion, or 6 with 12 zeros behind it), you can see that this is quite a distance. If we figure that even one star out of a thousand has some kind of intelligent life on its planets—and that may be much too hopeful a figure—it would still take a considerable amount of traveling before we could find another race.

Even if we could send ships to the stars and back, our prospect of finding such races would be relatively poor for a long time. Of course, we might be lucky and stumble on one almost at the beginning; or we might explore far more than a thousand suns before we found any advanced life at all. No matter how wonderful our rockets become, it might take us hundreds or even thousands of years to find another race.

We would have one clue to help us, however. When we begin moving out into space, we shall be sending radio signals between the planets. Even now we are shooting signals at the Moon and at other planets, trying to map them by radar. These signals are sent out at wave lengths that can pass through the atmosphere, and some of them are very strong.

On a fairly tight beam, a radio signal can travel a long way. A very advanced race might detect them many light-years away, and find our direction from the signal. When we get into space (where our atmosphere will not bother reception), we may eventually develop receiving devices sensitive enough to detect possible signals from other worlds. Naturally, our knowing the direction along which to look would make the discovery of other civilized races much easier and speedier.

One of the questions that has been asked again and again is probably running through your mind now, as it is running through mine.

If there are races of intelligent life among the stars, and if some are more advanced than we are, why have they not visited us, either recently or in the past?

We would expect it, certainly. Some of

the races "out there" should have had space travel for a long, long time, perhaps, if their worlds are a little older than ours. (After all, 100,000 years is only a short time in the history of a planet.) If the inhabitants ever had visited us—even many thousands of years ago—they should have noticed that intelligent life was developing on Earth, and kept a watch on this planet. If we found a race of even primitive cave-people on another world, we would drop by every few hundred years to see how they were progressing. By the time they could understand space travel—as we can now—we would surely make ourselves known to them.

The only logical answer is that, provided such travel between the stars is possible, those other races may have visited us again and again! They may have tried to get in touch with us before our time. It may have happened much more recently than we think—who knows?

Many very old legends persist. There is the story of Prometheus who brought fire from the Sun for mankind, as told by the Greeks. This story might have been one of how godlike beings came from the sky on ships spouting fire and gave some of that fire to the savages. There are stories of the Egyptian gods with their strange animal heads, and the other odd creatures of mythology—giants, one-eyed Cyclops, centaurs, men who rose into the heavens in fiery chariots that might easily have been rockets.

These tales prove nothing. They just could be fragments left from real stories of strange visits, but they could just as well be theories we worked out for ourselves, about the things we could not understand.

The important point is, however, that we would not know it if a real story of men in a rocket from the stars did get mixed into these tales, for such a story would be hidden in all the other myths.

Suppose such an event happened fairly recently? Well, even a few hundred years ago we would probably have no real account of it. If a spaceship had landed in the Middle Ages, the odd, nonhuman beings on board would have been called demons, and nothing could have been understood of the real facts. The only way we could have an account of such a visit would be by a very happy accident. The visitors would have to land in the right place and have the extreme good luck to encounter one of the few scholars of the day whose curiosity was stronger than his fears—perhaps a Roger Bacon, or someone like him.

As recently as 200 years ago—or in many sections of the world even today—any ship from space would no doubt be called the work of witches, demons or other horrible creatures.

On the other hand, perhaps a race may have been watching us without wanting to interfere until we get out into space on our own, in which case we would have no way of knowing it. (*Not* the flying saucers which keep showing themselves to us in such huge numbers! A race that was watching us from space could do so without our knowing, and would need only a single ship.

The truth is that we simply do not know. Probably, if there are races capable of traveling in space between the stars, none has been lucky enough to stumble on us, out of all the other suns it might visit.

We have no real evidence to believe that we have been visited in the past or will be in the future. We also have no reason to be sure there have not been such visits. To find the answers, we will have to go visiting among the stars ourselves, if we can.

It is nice to know that there is even a chance of other eyes watching the heavens, and of other races waiting out there for us to find them. It makes the Universe a lot less lonely than it seemed to be a few short years ago.

CHAPTER 20

to the stars

LONG before men have conquered all the planets, they will look up at the stars and vow that someday we will reach there and conquer the whole Universe! Men have been making the same kind of impossible promises to themselves for a long time.

We can imagine Ab, the first caveman to build a boat. By hard work and great heroism for his time, he has paddled out to an island half a mile beyond the shore. Now he is the first man ever to get so far, and he is full of pride. He turns his face toward the west and his face grows strong and resolute. "Someday," he promises himself, "I'll paddle right across the ocean and discover America!"

It would be easier for Ab to make good on his boast (if he had known there was an America) than for the first man on Mars to get to the stars, however. In fact, if Ab had kept paddling, living off fish, and had luck enough to run into no storms, yet have rainfall often enough for a water supply, he might have reached America in a year. No man could ever live long enough to reach the nearest star in any ship we could conceive of for the trip.

Pluto is a long, long way from us—so far that light, traveling at 186,000 miles every second, takes more than 5 hours to get from the Sun to Pluto. This distance is nothing compared to that to Proxima Centauri, our nearest neighboring star; to reach there, light takes more than 4 *years!*

Or to put it another way, the highest speed we will need to reach Mars is about 100,000 miles an hour, counting the speed we gain from Earth's motion about the Sun. At that speed, it would take us 27,000 years to reach Proxima Centauri, without ever slowing down. Other stars would require an even longer journey.

Suppose, however, we can build better and better rockets, using wonderful atomic engines and fuels that will give us 10,000 times as much speed as any rocket we can build today? That is a rather fantastic improvement, but we cannot say that it is totally impossible. If we achieve that speed, then maybe we can make the journey to the stars.

Well, let us see. Our present rockets will give us a speed of about 5 miles a second. On this new model rocket we are dreaming of, we could then reach a top speed of 50,000 miles a second. However, to have fuel enough to land, we would be able to use only half our fuel at the start; this amount would limit us to about 25,000 miles a second on the trip. After we built up top speed, the pull of the Sun would keep working for us, slowing us down a little. In such a case, we would still need about 50 years to make the trip.

To make things worse, we would have to equip the ship so that the men could live in it during all those years. This would mean less of the total weight could be taken up by the engines and fuel, in order to make room for the needs of the crew. That would cut the speed and make the trip longer.

The prospect looks rather hopeless. It seems that no man could take off for the stars and have any hope of returning to Earth to tell about it. That statement is quite true. In fact, when we work the problem out carefully, it appears that no man who started on the trip in any ship we can even imagine would live to reach Proxima Centauri, much less to return.

The distance by itself does not matter too much. Actually, we could no doubt build a ship that would reach the stars. Only a little more speed than that needed to reach the planets would be required to escape the Solar System completely. As the ship would get farther and farther away from the Sun, gravity would pull it back with less and less force. Most of the voyage would require very little energy to keep the ship moving.

It is the time involved that becomes all-important. If we followed the most economical road to the stars, in terms of fuel, the journey would take so long that we could not even think of such trips. The fastest trips we could hope to make would still require hundreds of years when everything is considered, before the returning rocket could again contact Earth.

All these drawbacks do *not* mean such a journey is totally impossible. A man's life span is not long enough for him to live through the experience. If we send whole families, though, the trip becomes worth considering. The original travelers may die on the way, but their children could carry on. Maybe the grandchildren would reach the star, explore it and begin the long trip back to our Sun. If there is a habitable planet there, they might set up a colony and beam the news back to us by radio. It would be quite possible to construct a station capable of beaming a signal back to Earth from Proxima Centauri, or even from a star quite a bit farther away.

To do this would require a very large ship to hold all the people. A crew of several hundred would be desirable. They would have to spend their whole lives in space, and be like a small village off by themselves. They would need animals for food, plants to give them breathable air and more food, libraries, and everything else that a community might need to be complete in itself. Power would be the least of their troubles, since a small atomic generator would provide all they could require, and such a generator would last for thousands of years, if properly designed.

The reason this method could work at all is that the ship would be like a small world, completely self-contained. The travelers would not run out of supplies, because nothing on such a ship would ever be lost. The air they breathe would supply carbon dioxide to the plants; the plants would release the oxygen back for use by the people. The food would be grown, and the human and animal wastes would go back to provide fertilizer for more plant growth. Water could be redistilled and used over and over again. Tools might break, but the metal could be reused.

Nothing would vanish, because there would be no place for anything to go. With enough energy from the atomic generator, everything would simply be used and re-used over and over again. It is the same way on Earth, where water falls as rain, runs to the sea, and then is lifted by evaporation to fall again as rain. In fact, such a spaceship would truly be a small world, and life on it could continue almost forever, without any need for greater initial supplies than would be required for a trip of a single year!

Such a ship would be built far out in space, where it would never have to fight against the heavy gravity of a planet. In this way, it could be constructed without too much weight, since no heavy strain from acceleration would be needed. It would never land on any planet around the star to which it headed, but would take up an orbit from which it could launch smaller ships that it would carry.

The people aboard would not be completely cut off from Earth, either. Fiction about such trips has been filled with accounts of mutiny, and of grandchildren who no longer believed that they had come from Earth, but this would not have to be true. Radio signals would be sent out from Earth to the ship, beamed by great transmitters that could keep in constant touch with each other. The men on the ship might even be able to send signals back. Such signals would take a long time to cover the vast distance, since radio waves travel at the same speed as light. The delay would not matter too much, however.

If a trip to one of the stars should uncover intelligent life, naturally further contact would be attempted. In that event, the ship might return to Earth, carrying families of the other race. Such a discovery would certainly stir up a tremendous interest in further travel to such a star.

However, such a method of traveling to the stars does not offer us many opportunities for real commerce. Our ships will go out, perhaps never to return. If they do return for use on another trip, it will be only after hundreds of years. Only a few families in any century will be able to set out for the stars, so such a journey will make almost no difference in the life of the average man.

With this kind of star travel in effect, there will be no great fleets busily trading between the stars. There will be no empires

of many stars. Likewise there cannot be any regular traffic between suns! All the things that are so common in much of science fiction are impossible without some means of moving from star to star at speeds even faster than light.

Is that possible? Men always manage to do more in one century than was dreamed of a century earlier. In this case, there is a limit. As far as we know, the speed of light is the fastest speed attainable in our Universe. No matter how good the ships and fuel we design may be, it does not seem likely that we will ever be able to travel as fast as light.

Albert Einstein gave us the reason, just as he gave us a formula that led to the use of atomic power. He showed us that anything that approaches the speed of light begins to increase its mass. Mass is the measure of matter. Near Earth we talk about the weight of matter, but when there is no weight, we call it mass. It still shows us how much inertia—resistance to change of speed and direction—matter will have, as well as some other properties.

The closer we get to the speed of light, the faster this increase of mass takes place. When we almost reach 186,000 miles a second, our mass rises so incredibly that it becomes nearly infinite—so great that there is no way of considering how great it is. Consequently its inertia would also become infinitely great—and obviously, with so much resistance to acceleration, getting the mass to go faster would be out of the question.

Of course, when we project ourselves far enough into the future, nobody can be sure of what will happen. Even the fantastic things we read about in science fiction now might come true. We might find a way to send bodies through space by some kind of radio transmission, known as *teleportation.* We might find some wholly new way to drive a spaceship, so that it would be able to move from star to star in a short time.

Science can give no answers to these hopes. Now they are only dreams that have no relation to the facts. We cannot discuss them seriously, since they are nothing but fantasy. Until we know more, we shall have to consider only what science can promise.

That is not too discouraging, after all. Science has shown us exactly how we can get out into space. It has already marked the way to the planets and told us some of the things we will find there, as well as how we can get there.

We will not have to wait too long for that journey, either. Probably men will land on another planet before the next century begins. Many people will live to see that achievement. Their children will live in an era where knowledge of other worlds will be as common as a knowledge of South America is to us now. Their grandchildren in turn will surely see things that we cannot even guess at clearly.

We even have reason to believe that someday in the future there will be men living on other planets around other stars, building colonies and growing in numbers until they will truly inhabit many of those worlds as we now inhabit our Earth. Maybe we cannot ever really conquer the whole Universe, but it seems that we may conquer a greater segment of it than the small section in which we began.

That is enough for us on which to dream. The future is cloudy in many ways, but it promises more now than it has promised at any other time throughout history. Whatever happens, we can be sure that the years ahead are going to be the most interesting ones any man has ever experienced.

We are about ready to go out into space—to the planets—even to the stars! What more can we ask?

INDEX